# GREAT EVENTS
## IN THE LIFE OF
## GEORGE WASHINGTON

**5** *Marries Martha Custis, 1759*

**6** *Takes command of the Continental Army, 1775*

**7** *Valley Forge, 1777-1778*

# THE STORY OF
# George Washington

*"The character, the counsels, and example of our Washington . . . will guide us through the doubts and difficulties that beset us; they will guide our children and our children's children in the paths of prosperity and peace, while America shall hold her place in the family of nations."*

—EDWARD EVERETT

*Washington at Valley Forge*

*To*

PETER BARNETT

*who helped me write this book by playing
very quietly whenever he came to visit
and found me working*

# Contents

# CONTENTS

# Illustrations

[ *ix* ]

# THE STORY OF
# George Washington

*"Whoa, Beauty!" George reined the big brown horse up short*

# CHAPTER ONE

## B-l-e-w Spells Blue

---

WHOA, BEAUTY!"

George reined the big brown horse up short. He spoke to the young man who was standing near the stable.

"Was that better, Austin?" he asked. "Did her hind hoofs clear the fence nicely that time?"

His brother nodded. "You ride well for a ten-year-old," he said.

George grinned. "I'll be eleven in six months," he declared. "And Beauty's an easy horse to ride."

He brushed a lock of sandy-red hair back from his eyes. "I'd like to give her a gallop down the river road before I turn her out to pasture," he said. "May I?"

Austin Washington shook his head. "I need her myself now, lad," he told the boy. "The ferry's just coming in. And I've an errand to do for Father in Fredericksburg."

"Will you stop at the apothecary's shop while you're there and get some candy?" George asked eagerly. He climbed out of the saddle. "Brown-sugar candy or white-sugar, Austin," he went on. "I don't care which."

Austin smiled. "Just so it's sweet!" he teased. "Yes, I'll bring some candy home, if I can."

He swung himself to Beauty's back. Then he started down the steep lane which led to the Rappahannock River.

There was a wharf at the end of the lane. The little ferryboat, which ran across the river to Fredericksburg and back, was just docking.

George waved his arm to the ferryman, who was a friend of his. And the man waved back in reply.

Just then two small boys came running from the dark red farmhouse beyond the

[4]

stable. A brown dog ran barking at their heels. Chickens, scratching in the dust, scurried out of their way. And a big black cat put up her back and puffed her tail as they passed her.

Both boys were shouting at the same time. "George! George Washington! Mother wants you. She wants you right away."

George waited until his brothers had reached him and he had quieted the dog. Then he asked, "What does she want, Jacky?"

The younger boy opened his mouth to reply. But eight-year-old Sam spoke up first.

"She says you haven't learned to spell the words that you missed in school yesterday," Sam announced. "You missed seven words and you have to learn them at once. You'd better hurry, too."

George slapped at a mosquito which had lighted on his cheek.

"Spelling!" he exclaimed in disgust. "I don't like to spell words." He looked around unhappily.

It was a beautiful Saturday morning. Far too fine a morning to sit indoors studying spelling. The September sun shone brightly on the lovely Virginia countryside. And there were many things he wanted to do.

He wanted to go for a swim in the river. And to teach the black colt in the pasture to run at the end of a rope. He wanted to watch the Negroes at work in his father's tobacco fields. And to go exploring in the woods not far from the house.

He wanted to climb to the top of the tallest cherry tree. And then, when he was tired of climbing, he wanted to lie in the grassy meadow, planning what he would be when he grew up.

But his mother said he must study his spelling lesson. And he knew he must obey her promptly. Everyone on Ferry Farm obeyed Mrs. Washington when she gave an order. George started slowly toward the house.

It was not a big house. But it was comfortable looking, with tall pine trees growing close by. Near the house were several smaller buildings.

There was a dairy where an old Negro woman was churning butter and another was washing clothes. There were three sheds where tobacco was stored. There was a smoke-house. And there was the little building which was the kitchen.

George stuck his head in the door of the kitchen. Sarah, the cook, was standing over the fire, stirring something in a big kettle. She smiled and laid down her long-handled spoon when she saw George.

[7]

"I reckon you's as hungry as you always is," she declared with a chuckle. "You just wait a minute."

She stuck her hand into a brown jar and pulled out a biscuit. Then she smeared it with honey and handed it to George.

"Here. Maybe this will help to fill up them long, hollow legs of yours," she said.

George laughed. He finished the biscuit in two bites and ran around the house.

His sister, nine-year-old Betty, was sitting on the low front steps. Charley, the youngest Washington child, was with her. They were playing together with a tiny yellow kitten.

George leaned down and scratched the kitten behind its ears. Then he went indoors to his mother's room at the end of the wide hall.

Mrs. Washington was waiting for him. She brushed his hair back from his face and straightened his collar.

"I'm glad you came quickly," she said. "Law! Your hands are dirty, George! There's fresh water in that pitcher over there. And your copybook is on the table. Wash well and get to work. I must get to my mending or I will never have it finished."

She bustled out of the room. George poured some water into the china basin and washed his hands. Then he sat down at the table and pulled his copybook toward him.

"B-l-u-e, blue," he spelled softly. "B-l-u-e, blue."

His eyes went to the open window. Through it he could see a patch of sky.

"I wonder if the ocean's as blue as that sky," he thought. "I'll see it some day. When I sail to England to go to school the way Austin and Lawrence did. I'll see it, then. And then I'll know."

He wriggled in his chair and sighed. Then he looked at his lesson again.

[9]

"Blue," he said to himself. "B-l-e-w spells blue. I wish Lawrence would come home from the war. I wonder where he's fighting now."

George pushed his book aside. He leaned his head on his hand and stared straight ahead. His spelling was forgotten. He was thinking about his eldest brother.

[*10*]

He had not seen Lawrence for nearly two years. Not since the day Lawrence had sailed away for foreign lands to help England fight against Spain.

How fine Lawrence had looked in his captain's uniform, with his shiny sword! How kind he was! How friendly! And how full of fun! He was brave, too. Very brave.

"When I grow up I want to be just like him," George thought soberly. "Whatever I do, I want to be just like Lawrence."

Suddenly he gave a little start. "Why, Lawrence will think I'm a great baby if I can't spell easy words like these, when he comes home," he said to himself. And he pulled his copybook closer and began to study hard.

# CHAPTER TWO

## *Lawrence Comes Home*

---

IT WAS EARLY in the afternoon. A few flakes of snow drifted slowly past the windows of the Ferry Farm dining room. In the big fireplace the flames leaped high.

Mr. Washington stood behind his chair at the head of the table. He looked around at his family. Then he bowed his head and closed his eyes.

"God bless us in what we are about to receive," he prayed. "Amen."

"Amen," said eight voices all at once.

Sam nudged George with his elbow. "You didn't say 'Amen,' " he said, as he sat down in his chair.

[*12*]

George did not answer him. He was too excited to speak.

Lawrence was home! After two long years at war Captain Lawrence Washington had come home at last. There he sat on the other side of the table, between Betty and Jack. And George couldn't take his eyes from him.

Lawrence unfolded his napkin and pinned it under his chin. He turned to his father.

"And how was the tobacco crop this year,

sir?" he asked. "Is all going well on our plantations?"

"Very well indeed," Mr. Washington replied. He picked up his carving knife and began to cut slices from the big ham on the platter in front of him.

"We've shipped two dozen hogsheads of fine tobacco to England already," he went on. "There is more in the storehouses. But we want to hear about you, and about Admiral Vernon. Did you find him a good leader?"

"The best in the world," Lawrence Washington declared. And he began to tell about Admiral Vernon and the battles he had fought in the West Indies.

George leaned forward, listening intently. He could hardly wait to begin asking questions.

The Negro servant set a plate of food before him. But the boy did not see it. He did not even hear his mother speak to him. At last Mrs. Washington touched his arm.

"George, stop staring at your brother," she

commanded him. "Eat your ham and pota-
toes. Everyone else has finished and Susie's
waiting to bring on the pudding."

George looked around at the empty plates.
Then he picked up his fork quickly and began
to eat. At that moment Lawrence smiled at
him across the table.

"I believe you've grown a foot since I saw
you last!" he exclaimed.

George shook his head and swallowed a big
mouthful of meat.

"Not a foot," he said, as soon as he could
speak. "Only about five and a half inches.
Lawrence, how many yards will a cannon ball
travel?"

Lawrence looked puzzled. "I don't know,"
he replied.

He turned to his father. "I see the boy still
has his head full of figures," he remarked. "Is
he as good now at arithmetic as he was when
I went away?"

"Yes," Mr. Washington replied, looking
proudly at George. "I met Mr. Marye in Fred-

[15]

ericksburg just last week. And he told me George could add a row of figures faster than any other boy in his school.''

"He can run faster than any of the boys in school, too,'' Jack added. "Even the big ones. And he can jump higher, and—''

"But he's not very good at spelling,'' Sam broke in. "He misses—''

"You hold your tongue!'' George cried angrily. In a flash he had turned on his brother. "You don't have to talk about that, the first day Lawrence is home. I'll—''

He sprang to his feet with his arm upraised. Sam ducked just in time. Mr. Washington spoke quickly.

"Watch your temper, George,'' he commanded. "Sit down at once, or leave the table.''

Tears of rage had rushed to George's eyes. He brushed them away hastily and sat down.

"I—I study my spelling, Lawrence,'' he said, as soon as he could speak. "I want to set the words down right. But sometimes the letters don't make sense the way numbers do.''

[16]

"That's right," Lawrence agreed. "Sometimes they don't. T-h-r-o-u-g-h is 'through'
and r-o-u-g-h is 'rough.' There's no sense to
it at all. But you'll learn if you keep on trying. I'll help you." He smiled. "Now, aren't
you sorry you tried to knock poor Sam's head
off?"

George nodded soberly. He looked at Sam
and grinned slowly. "You can be captain in
my place when we play tug-of-war after school
tomorrow," he promised.

"I'll be captain if you'll play on my side,"
Sam said happily. "Then we'll be sure to—"
He broke off suddenly. "Hey, look!" he cried,
pointing to the window. "Here comes Aunt
Mildred up the path from the ferry."

"And Uncle Henry, too," Jack added. "I'll
let them in."

He jumped up from his chair. So did Sam.
Both boys ran to open the door.

Aunt Mildred and Uncle Henry Willis had
come from Fredericksburg to see Lawrence.
They told him how glad they were that he
had returned safely from the war. And they

[*17*]

asked him all kinds of questions about the fighting and the foreign countries he had seen.

Sam and Jack and Charley and Betty soon grew tired of listening to the grownups talk. So they went outside to play. But George stayed close to Lawrence until the afternoon was over, and the visitors had gone home. Then he picked up Lawrence's sword, which stood in the corner near the stairs.

"May I try it on?" he asked eagerly. "Just to see how it feels?"

Lawrence nodded. "If you're careful," he replied.

He helped George strap on the sword. The scabbard was so long it almost touched the floor. With his hand on the hilt of the sword, George walked proudly across the room and back again. Then he pulled the sword from its black leather scabbard and carefully felt its sharp, shining blade.

Mrs. Washington was lighting the tall candles on the mantelpiece. She watched the boy uneasily.

*George pulled the sword from its scabbard and felt its
sharp, shining blade*

"Put that dreadful thing up, son," she said at last. "One soldier in this family is enough. Swords and fighting are not for you if I can prevent it. Put it up, I say. Then call Betty and the boys in for supper."

So George gave the sword back to Lawrence and went to call the younger children in from play.

That night he climbed into bed beside Sam as usual. Sam was soon sleeping soundly. But George lay awake for a long time, staring into the dark.

He was remembering all the stories Lawrence had told that day. In his mind he was hearing the roar of cannon. He was seeing the blaze of gunfire. And when sleep came to him at last, he had a splendid dream. He dreamed he was charging into battle on a fine white horse, waving a shining sword in the air.

## CHAPTER THREE

## *The* London Belle *from England*

GEORGE OPENED the front door and stepped outside. He sniffed the air eagerly. It smelled of freshly plowed earth and cherry blossoms and wet pine needles. White clouds scudded across the blue, blue sky. The shiny new leaves on the trees danced in the wind.

Breakfast was over. But the other Washington children were not yet ready to start off for school. George could hear Sam inside the house, telling Betty that he could not find his copybook.

"If I hurry I'll have time to climb the big oak tree and take a look at the world," George thought suddenly. He cleared the steps in one jump and dashed across the dewy grass to the huge oak which stood near by.

[ *21* ]

Quickly he swung himself up to the lowest limb. Then he climbed through the branches like a squirrel until he had almost reached the top of the tree. Bracing his back against the trunk, he looked around.

Through the little new leaves he could see all of Ferry Farm spread out below him. In the tobacco fields five Negroes were hard at work. Three other Negroes were working in the vegetable garden.

[22]

Tom, the stableboy, was leading two of the horses out to pasture. And near the stable door, Austin and Lawrence stood talking with their father.

Mr. Washington had his hand on the bridle of a big gray mare. He was dressed for a journey.

Mr. Augustine Washington was not a rich man. But, like many men in the colony of Virginia, he owned more than one plantation. He was part owner of an iron mine and forge, too. His plantations and the ironworks kept him very busy. And he was often away from home.

"I hope he won't stay long this time," George thought. "When Father's away, Lawrence and Austin have so much to do that I hardly ever see them."

He watched the three men for a minute. Then he turned his head and looked the other way.

At the foot of the bluff below him the deep water of the Rappahannock River sparkled in the sunlight. The steeple of the church in

Fredericksburg on the opposite shore shone brightly. So did the billowing white sails on the big ship just rounding the bend in the river.

George squinted his blue-gray eyes and peered sharply at the ship. At the English flag flying from the masthead. At the carved figurehead on the prow.

Suddenly he gave a low cry of delight. Grinning broadly, he climbed quickly down from the tree and raced toward the stable.

"Father!" he shouted. "Father, wait. Don't go! The *London Belle*'s coming! The *London Belle!* She's—she's sailing up the river now."

"The *London Belle*'s coming! The *London Belle* from England!"

The words spread like wildfire around Ferry Farm. Mr. Washington's journey was forgotten. School was forgotten! Work was forgotten! The Negroes left the fields. Even busy Mrs. Washington dropped what she was doing. And everyone started down the steep path to the river.

George was the first to reach the shore. The

ship was now so close that he could hear the captain shouting orders. He could see the sailors running about the decks, pulling ropes and furling sails.

It seemed to the impatient boy that the ship would never land. But at last she was made fast to the long wharf. And the captain was shaking hands with all the grown-up Washingtons.

He gave them the letters and messages he had brought to them from their relatives and friends in England. Then he began to tell about his voyage across the Atlantic Ocean. And about the places where he had stopped on his way up the Rappahannock River.

George wanted to listen. But even more, he wanted to watch the sailors. They had already begun to bring exciting-looking boxes up from the hold in the ship.

One by one they set them down on the wharf. George and the other children gathered around them quickly, trying to guess what each box contained.

"That box has tea in it," Betty declared.

[25]

*He watched anxiously as the men rolled each
big hogshead to the ship*

"But Father sent for these things so long ago that I can't remember what else he ordered. I hope he'll open them for us right away."

"He won't," George declared. "I just heard the captain tell him that he wants to get under sail as soon as he can. This is his last stop on the river.

"Father has sixteen barrels of tobacco to be loaded on the ship before she leaves. He says there's lots to do. We won't have time for school today. Here, Sam, help me with this box and we'll carry it up to the house."

George picked up one end of the box. Sam took the other. Together they started up the path. Before long all the boxes had been carried from the wharf.

Then the Negroes began to bring the tobacco from the storehouse and to load it on the ship. Mr. Washington and Lawrence kept sharp eyes on the work. So did Austin.

George stood beside his father at the top of the bluff. He watched anxiously, too, as the men rolled each big hogshead down the riverbank, and along the wharf to the ship.

[ 27 ]

He knew that they would be very careful to get the tobacco safely aboard. For tobacco was used as money in the colony of Virginia. And George's father was sending this tobacco to England to pay for the things in the boxes which had just arrived.

It was late afternoon before those boxes were opened at last. Everyone in the family gathered around as Mr. and Mrs. Washington unpacked them.

Out came new bonnets and yards of fine material for Sunday dresses and jackets. Shining gilt buttons, a cocked hat for Austin, tools, dishes, and tea.

A book in Latin for Lawrence, medicines, and a box of spices. Needles, thread, a looking glass, worsted stockings, and shoes. And last of all a pair of black leather pumps, with silver buckles on them, for George.

He sat down on the floor and tried them on at once.

"Do they fit?" his mother asked anxiously. She leaned over and felt the toe of one pump. Then she shook her head at Mr. Washington.

"The boy is growing too fast," she complained. "In a month these pumps will be too small."

Mr. Washington laughed. "Never mind," he said. "He can wear them when he goes to Chotank and when he's outgrown them he can give them to Sam."

"Chotank!" George exclaimed in surprise. He looked up eagerly. He liked to visit his uncle's plantation on the shore of the Potomac River. "Am I really going to Chotank?"

His father nodded. "I promised your cousins the last time I saw them that you could visit them this spring," he said. "If all goes well, Henry will ride over with you some day next week."

So early one morning the following week, George said good-by to his family. And off he rode on one of his father's horses, toward Chotank.

Henry, an old Negro servant, followed on another horse, with George's luggage strapped to the saddle behind him.

The boy whistled softly as he and Henry

trotted along the country road. He was thinking of the good times he would soon be having
with his cousins.

And he did have good times at Chotank.
But the visit ended suddenly—and very sadly.

# CHAPTER FOUR

## *Great Changes Come to Ferry Farm*

---

GEORGE WOKE with a start. He sat up
and looked around. He was not in the big
four-poster bed with his cousin Robin at Chotank. He was in his own bed at home. Suddenly he remembered why.

"My father's dead!" he thought soberly.
And he lay down and buried his face in his
pillow.

It had happened very suddenly. One minute, George remembered, he was pitching
quoits with Robin at Chotank. And the next
minute Henry had come galloping across the
grass, with his horse in a lather.

"Your father's sick to dyin', Marse George,"
Henry had said, looking very solemn. "Your

[*31*]

mother wants you to come home right quick!"

So now George was at home again. And his strong, kind, cheerful, loving father was dead. It was hard to believe.

Mr. Washington had divided most of his property among his three oldest sons. To Lawrence he had left the plantation on the Potomac River called Little Hunting Creek. To Austin he left the farm at Wakefield, where

George had been born. To George he left
Ferry Farm.

"But Ferry Farm won't really belong to you
until you're grown up," Lawrence explained
to George.

"I know it," George said gravely. "Not till
I'm twenty-one. But we can all go right on living here forever, can't we?"

Lawrence shook his head.

"Not forever," he said with a little smile.
"Austin and I both want to get married some
day and start homes of our own. But wher-
ever we are, we'll help Mother and you and
the younger children all that we can."

It was not very long after this that both Lawrence and Austin moved to the plantations
which their father had given them. And for a
while Ferry Farm seemed a lonely place to
George.

However, a boy cannot be lonely for long
when he has a sister and three younger brothers. And a river to fish in. And horses to ride.
And lessons to learn. And a hundred and one
other things to do.

[*33*]

The summer days passed quickly. Fall came and went. Snow began to fly. And soon George was twelve years old. Then almost before he knew it, he was thirteen. He was growing so fast that none of his clothes seemed to fit him any more.

This worried him. He liked fine clothes. He liked to look well dressed when he went to visit Austin or Lawrence.

Both young men were married now, each to a girl named Anne. Austin and his Anne were living at Wakefield. Lawrence and his Anne were living on the plantation at Little Hunting Creek.

Lawrence had built a fine new house on his plantation. He had named it Mount Vernon, in honor of Admiral Vernon, who had been his commander during the war with Spain. And how George loved to visit there!

Lawrence's wife, Anne Fairfax Washington, was the daughter of a wealthy man. She and Lawrence had many friends. Life at Mount Vernon was gay and exciting. It was different from anything George had ever known before.

There were big dinner parties, with the ladies dressed in beautiful gowns and the gentlemen in fine suits of satin and velvet. There were fox hunts and dances and card games. The house seemed to be full of guests most of the time.

Many of these guests were officers in the British Army or Navy. They talked with Lawrence Washington of battles on land and at sea. George listened eagerly to all their stories.

Whenever Lawrence was speaking George watched him carefully. He still wanted to grow up to be just like Lawrence. To wear fine clothes. To live in a beautiful house. To own land. To have many friends. And to know how to behave in company. Especially to know how to behave in company.

He was never quite sure what to do when he entered a room full of people. Or how to act when he sat down at Lawrence's big dinner table. He thought about this whenever he came home to Ferry Farm after a visit to Mount Vernon.

One fall day, after such a visit, he waited impatiently for school to close. Then he raced

*In Lawrence's home at Mount Vernon life was gay and exciting*

through the streets of Fredericksburg to the ferry. As soon as the little boat had crossed the river, he sped up the path to the house. He opened the front door quickly and bumped right into Betty.

"Look!" he exclaimed, waving a little book under her nose.

But before she could even get a peek at the book, he started up the stairs three at a time. Betty picked up her skirts and followed him to his room.

"What is that book, George?" she asked. "What do you have there?"

"Just what I want!" George replied joyfully. "A set of rules to tell me how to behave in company. I mean to copy every one."

"How many are there?" Betty asked, peering over his shoulder at the book.

"One hundred and ten," George announced. "I'll read you some of them. Listen."

He turned over the pages. "Here's a good one," he said. And he began to read.

" 'If you cough, sneeze, sigh, or yawn, do it

[37]

not loud, but privately; and speak not in your yawning, but put your handkerchief or hand before your face and turn aside.' "

Betty nodded and sat down on the bed beside him. "Read another," she demanded.

" 'In the presence of others sing not to yourself with a humming noise,' " George read. " 'Nor drum with your fingers or feet.

" 'Take no salt or cut bread with your knife greasy. If you soak bread in the sauce, let it be no more than what you can put in your mouth at a time. And blow not your broth at table, but stay till it cools of itself.

" 'Put not meat to your mouth with your knife in your hand. Neither spit forth the stones of any fruit pie upon a dish, nor cast anything under the table.

" 'If anyone come to speak to you while you are sitting, stand up—' " He broke off suddenly.

"See!" he exclaimed. "They're fine rules! They tell me just how to behave when I'm visiting Lawrence. Now I'm going to begin copying them."

[*38*]

Soon he was seated at a table with a quill pen in his hand. His copybook lay open before him. He dipped his pen into his pewter inkwell. And with great care he wrote these words:

*Rules of Civility and Decent Behaviour in Company and Conversation*

Sitting back in his chair, he looked at the words with a broad smile. Then he pulled the book of rules toward him and went to work.

# CHAPTER FIVE

## *A Busy Afternoon*

---

IT WAS a fine day the following spring. A warm day for early March. A little wind blew up the river, making the water ripple and sparkle in the sun. Tiny waves slapped against the bow of the rowboat, as George pulled strongly on his oars.

At last he took the oars from the water and rested them across his knees, letting the boat drift with the current. He grinned at Sam, who was sitting in the stern of the boat.

"I'm sorry poor Mr. Marye had such a bad toothache," he said with a chuckle. "But I'm glad he had to let school out early."

"So am I," Sam agreed. "I'm glad Mother and Betty took Jack and Charley to Aunt Mildred's, too. Now we have the whole afternoon to ourselves.

"We've only rowed about half a mile. Let's go on up the river to the falls."

George shook his head. "I'm going swimming," he announced.

"Swimming!" Sam repeated in amazement. "You know Mother'd never let you go swimming in March." He dipped his hand in the water. "Anyway, it's too cold," he added.

George laughed. "You talk like a baby!" he exclaimed. "It's not too cold for me. Here, you take my place at the oars and I'll dive from the stern."

[*41*]

Sam looked doubtful, but he changed places with his brother. George stripped off his jacket and bent over to take off his shoes. A moment later he plunged into the water.

He came up gasping, several yards from the boat.

"You were—right, Sammy!" he called. "It's —it's *icy* cold. You've got a head start there. I'll race you—to the shore."

With strong, steady strokes, George struck out for the bank. Sam picked up the oars and rowed for all he was worth. He ran the bow of the boat up on the sand just as George's feet touched the river bottom.

"I won!" Sam cried.

George nodded. He splashed toward shore, beating his long arms across his chest. As he passed the boat, he grabbed his clothes.

When he reached land, he dried himself quickly on his shirt. Then he pulled on his knee breeches and jacket. His lips were blue. And his teeth were chattering, even after he had put on his stockings and shoes.

"That was a f-f-foolheaded thing for

m-me to d-do," he said, as he fastened the buckles on his breeches. "M-Mother will g-g-give me a good p-piece of her mind when she hears about it."

"I'll never tell her," Sam declared. "You don't have to, either."

"I will—if she asks me," George said. He squeezed some water out of his hair.

"If you'll r-r-row the b-boat back to our landing, I'll r-run home across the f-f-fields," he stammered. "I'll warm up f-faster that way."

Sam nodded. "Then you can put on a dry shirt before anyone sees you, too," he said. Pushing the boat into the water, he climbed in and picked up the oars.

George scrambled up the bank and started across the fields at a run. He was still chilly when he reached home. As he took a shirt from the chest where he kept his clothing, he shivered, and sneezed three times.

"Stupid!" he said half aloud. He was not at all pleased with himself. For he knew that he always caught cold easily, and that he had done a very foolish thing. He didn't know why he had done it, either. For a moment he felt restless and unhappy.

"Here I am, fourteen years old, and sometimes I don't show as much sense as Charley," he scolded himself.

"I wish I were a man. I'm tired of studying at my books and playing with younger boys. I want to work with men and earn money."

He picked up a towel and rubbed his wet hair. At the same time he glanced out of the window. In an instant his unhappiness was forgotten.

Tossing the towel onto his bed, he grabbed his jacket. Then he raced down the stairs and out to the stable yard.

Tom, the stableman, was leading a prancing brown colt around the yard. He tried to hold the horse still when he saw George.

"Satan's sure feeling mighty frisky today," he said. "But he's broke fine to his bridle and saddle now."

George nodded. He put out his hand to stroke Satan's neck. The horse jerked his head

[44]

away. George pulled a piece of brown-sugar candy from his pocket. He held it out on the palm of his hand. Satan sniffed it warily and then closed his soft lips on it.

"Good boy," George said in a low voice. He ran his hand over Satan's neck and patted him, talking to him all the while. Then he took hold of the saddle.

Tom eyed the boy uneasily. "You ain't figurin' to ride Satan yet, is you, Marse George?" he asked. "He's plumb full of meanness today. And you know he ain't never had anyone on his back."

"I know it," George said. "But it's time he did. He's a good horse. I can handle him."

He put his foot into the stirrup and sprang lightly into the saddle. "Watch out!" he cried.

Tom let go of the bridle at once and quickly stepped out of the way. Satan reared on his hind legs and pawed the air. Then he turned sharply and bolted through the open gate into the meadow on the other side of the road.

Suddenly he stopped short. He lowered his head and kicked his heels up in the air. He

[45]

reared again, and plunged and twisted and
turned, trying to shake off his rider.

Tom looked worried. He spoke to another
Negro who had come to watch the struggle.

"That boy!" he exclaimed. "Seems like he
ain't afeard of nothin'. Look at him stick to
that horse."

The other man nodded. "He's goin' to get
hurt, though. That Satan's a mean one. He'll
throw the boy, for sure."

But Satan didn't throw George, although
he tried hard with every trick he knew.
George stuck fast in the saddle, with a firm
hold on the reins. Again and again he forced
the horse from a wild gallop to a walk. He

[46]

made him turn and stand and go and stop.

At last the battle was over. George pulled the quivering horse up by the stable-yard gate. The boy was panting for breath, but he grinned at the men who had been watching him.

"Look!" he said. "I have him well under control now. All he needs is a good run to tire him out."

He pressed his legs against the horse's sides. "Come on, boy, come on," he said.

Satan set off down the road at a canter. Then he broke into a gallop. His hoofs pounded the earth. His mane and tail streamed in the wind. George did not try to hold him in.

On and on Satan ran. The wind whistled in George's ears. It tore at his hair. His breath came fast, and he wanted to shout with joy. He felt as though he were part of this flying horse. And the horse seemed to sense that he had found a master.

When George pulled strongly on the reins and said, "Whoa," Satan came to a stop at

[47]

once. George patted the quivering horse and talked to him softly for several minutes. Then off they started once more.

Nearly an hour passed before the boy and the horse reached home. As they rode into the stable yard, Tom came running to meet them. Sam was with him.

"Whew, you were gone a long time!" Sam exclaimed. "I thought that Satan had tossed you and run away. But Tom said you were handling him fine."

George laughed. "Satan wouldn't throw me," he declared, swinging himself out of the saddle. "We're friends. We just stopped for a bit to watch some men working up the road."

He stroked Satan's soft nose. "Take him, Tom, and rub him down well," he said. "He's had a good run. I'm going back to watch those men again."

"I'll go with you," Sam announced. "What are they doing?"

George sneezed. "Surveying," he replied. "Maybe they'll show me how they do it.

Maybe they might even let me help them."

With Sam at his heels, George set off up the road. The sun was low in the sky when the two returned to Ferry Farm. Mrs. Washington, Betty, Jack, and Charley had come home from Aunt Mildred's house in Fredericksburg. And supper was almost ready.

But George wasn't very hungry. His head had begun to ache and his throat felt scratchy. He sniffled as he came into the dining room.

Mrs. Washington looked at him sharply.

"You have another cold!" she exclaimed. "How on earth did you get it?"

George tried to choke back a sneeze. "It's just a liddle one, Mudder," he said quickly. "You see, I wed swibbig and—"

"Swimming!" his mother repeated in dismay. "In March! George, you haven't as much sense as little Charley. Get yourself upstairs to bed as fast as you can, while I fix you a good dose of boneset tea."

George made a face at the thought of boneset tea. Then, with a sheepish grin at Sam, he went slowly upstairs to his bed.

[*49*]

## CHAPTER SIX

### *Lawrence's Plan*

---

JACKY WASHINGTON stood in the doorway of his mother's storeroom. He wondered
why George was in there, poking around
among the old pots and pans and dusty furni-
ture.

"What are you looking for?" he asked.

George coughed and shoved aside a bat-
tered washtub.

"This," he replied. And he pulled a long
wooden box out from under a broken butter-
churn. Then he squatted on his heels and
tugged at the lid until he got the box open.

Jacky squatted down beside him. "What's
in it?" he said.

"Surveying instruments," George answered. "They belonged to Father, and Mother said I could have them. I'm going to study hard and learn to be a surveyor, and earn a lot of money, Jacky. All I need to know is—"

Jack interrupted. "What's a surveyor?" he asked.

"A man who measures land and makes maps," George explained patiently. "I watched some of the surveyors at work last week. And this afternoon, too. They let me hold the chain they measure with, and carry their rods."

He had thrown back the lid of the box, and now he was looking over the instruments packed inside it.

"Everything's here," he said happily. "Come on outdoors with me, and watch me set up the tripod."

He picked up the box. With Jacky at his heels, he went outside.

Past the kitchen the two boys walked together. Past the dairy. Past the storehouses and the cow barns and the stable. Down the road between fields green with new tobacco. And out into an open meadow.

"Here's a good place to begin," George said, putting down his box. He pulled out the tripod and unfolded its long legs. Then he set it up carefully and screwed the compass in place.

"What's that for?" Jacky asked.

But George didn't answer. He had almost

forgotten that Jacky was there. Already he was hard at work, trying to survey the meadow.

That evening, after the younger children were in bed, George made his map of the meadow. When it was finished he laid down his pen. Picking up a little jar from the table, he shook some sand over the wet ink to dry it.

Then he studied the map carefully by the light of the flickering candle. At last he shook his head and sighed impatiently.

"It's not very good," he told his mother, who was sitting near him. "Look!"

Mrs. Washington laid down the stocking she was mending and took the map.

"You've drawn it with great care," she said. "And you've lettered it nicely."

"But it's not right!" George cried angrily. "I don't ever want to do anything if I can't do it right!"

Snatching the map, he tore it in two. Then he sprang from his chair and rushed out into the summer night, slamming the door behind him.

He was back almost at once. "I—I'm sorry that I stormed at you, Mother," he declared soberly. "It's not your fault that the map is wrong. Sometimes my—my temper still gets the best of me. Good night."

Picking up one of the candles, he started toward the stairs.

"Good night," his mother said. "Don't be downhearted about your map."

George turned and smiled. "I'm not downhearted," he told her. "Tomorrow I'll try it again and I'll keep on trying until it's right."

Shielding his candle with his hand, he began to climb the stairs.

Mrs. Washington watched him for a moment. How big he was! All arms and legs, and nearly as tall as his father had been! She was proud of him. But she was worried about him, too.

Sometimes he did things that frightened her. He was forever wanting to swim in the river where the current ran swiftest. To wrestle with boys far older and stronger than himself. To ride horses which no one else could

*Mrs. Washington took the map. "You've drawn it with great care," she said*

master. She did not understand why he wanted to run such risks. Often she did not know how to manage him.

"He needs a man to guide him," she thought. "I wish his father were alive." With a sigh she picked up her mending and went back to work.

Mrs. Washington was not the only one who was worried about young George. Lawrence was worried, also. One evening that summer, when he and his wife were sitting in the garden at Mount Vernon, he spoke about this.

"George is a clever lad," Lawrence said to Anne. "He wants to make something of himself and he works hard at everything he does."

Anne Washington nodded. "He'll grow into a fine man if only he has the right training," she said.

"Yes," Lawrence agreed. "But what is the right training for him? I wonder—" He broke off suddenly. "I pray you'll excuse me, my dear!" he exclaimed. "I've just thought of a splendid idea. I must write to the boy and to his mother about it at once."

He hurried into the house and sat down at his desk.

Several days later George and his mother received the letters which Lawrence Washington had written. George's eyes shone with joy and excitement as he read the letter which had come to him. But Mrs. Washington's face was gloomy. For Lawrence had said in his letters that he thought George should leave home and go to sea.

Perhaps George could enlist in the British Navy, Lawrence had written. If he worked hard he might some day become an officer. The training aboard ship was excellent. He would see something of the world. And the life was full of adventure.

In his letters Lawrence had also written that he had many friends in the British Navy. One of them would help George get a good start. He was sure of that. Did George like the idea? And what did Mrs. Washington think about it?

Did George like the idea! Already he could see himself standing on the quarter-deck

[ 57 ]

shouting orders, while bullets whistled past his ears. So could his mother. And she shook her head firmly.

"Lawrence must have taken leave of his senses!" she exclaimed to George. "The life at sea is too rough for any son of mine. It's full of danger and—"

"But I'm not afraid of danger," George broke in. "I *want* to go! Please give me leave!"

Again Mrs. Washington shook her head. And again George begged her to let him write to Lawrence that he was ready to go to sea.

He begged so hard and so often during the next few weeks that at last his mother made him a promise.

"I'll write to your Uncle Joseph Ball in England," she said. "And I'll ask him what he thinks of Lawrence's plan. If he thinks it's a wise one, then perhaps you may go."

So off went a letter to Uncle Joseph Ball on the next ship that sailed to England. Many months passed before his answer reached Ferry Farm.

When it came at last, Mrs. Washington

read it with joy and relief. For Uncle Joseph had written that he thought a sailor's life was no better than a dog's life. He said George should stay at home and be a tobacco planter. He should never go to sea.

George read the letter and shrugged his shoulders. He wasn't greatly disappointed. He really didn't care much now about becoming a sailor. He had been working hard at his surveying. And he loved it.

He had surveyed all the fields near his home. He had carried his instruments with him whenever he went to visit at Chotank, or Wakefield, or Mount Vernon. He had studied every book on surveying that he could find.

Now he could measure and figure and make maps very well indeed. Almost as well as the surveyors who had been working near by. And it was soon to prove lucky for George that this was so.

## CHAPTER SEVEN

## *An Exciting Invitation*

CHARLEY SAT on the edge of his brother's bed. He was watching George and Betty pack a little leather trunk.

"Are you really going to live at Mount Vernon forever?" he asked unhappily. "Aren't you ever coming home?"

George laughed. "Yes, Master Longface, of course I'm coming home," he replied, giving Charley a poke in the ribs. "I'll come home often to visit. But I am really going to live at Mount Vernon."

He turned to Betty, who was folding up a linen shirt. His eyes were shining.

"I still can't believe it!" he exclaimed. "I never thought Mother would let me go. Not even when Lawrence wrote that he was sick and needed me."

"Neither did I think she would," Betty said, laying the shirt in the trunk. "But she knows how lonesome Lawrence and Anne have been since their baby died and—"

She broke off suddenly. "Oh, I *wish* you weren't going!" she exclaimed. "I'm going to miss you dreadfully. We all will."

"I'll miss you, too," George said. "But just think, Bet, Lawrence is going to let me take fencing lessons. I'll go fox hunting, and learn to dance. And I can go on with my surveying and—"

"And you'll have fine clothes to wear," Betty broke in. "And your own horse to ride. I wish I were you. Here, don't forget this."

She handed George the book of rules for behavior which he had copied many months earlier. Just then she spied a small case in one corner of the trunk.

"What's in that little case?" she asked.

George's face turned red. "A razor," he replied in a low voice.

"A razor!" Betty repeated. She laughed. "What for?" she teased. "You're not big enough to need a razor yet!"

"I will be soon," George declared, trying to sound grown up. "Don't forget, Miss Betty Washington, I'll be sixteen next February."

He laid his copybook on top of a pair of fawn-colored knee breeches, beside a small pile of neatly folded handkerchiefs. Then he looked around the room to make sure that he had not forgotten anything.

"Well, everything's packed," he announced. And he closed his trunk.

Soon it was time for him to leave, and he was saying good-by.

Mrs. Washington wiped away some tears when she stood on tiptoe to kiss her tall young son. It was hard for her to let the boy leave home. But she had always wanted George to have the best of everything—as long as he did not run into danger.

She had not been able to send him to school in England. And she knew that Lawrence could give him a better start in life than he would get on Ferry Farm.

Lawrence Washington was becoming an important man in the colony of Virginia. He had made many wealthy and important friends. One of these friends was an English lord named Thomas Fairfax.

Lord Fairfax had been in America only a short time. But George had already heard about him from Lawrence and Anne, for he was a distant cousin of Anne's. He was visiting on Anne's father's plantation, right next to Mount Vernon. He was planning to build a home in Virginia. And he owned more than five million acres of good Virginia land.

Five *million* acres! It made George's head spin just to think of it. He was eager to see Lord Fairfax. But he was almost afraid to meet him.

"I'm not sure I'd know how to behave before such a great lord," George told Lawrence, soon after he had reached Mount Vernon.

Lawrence laughed. "Five million acres of land doesn't make Lord Fairfax very different from any other man," he said. "We'll ride over to Belvoir tomorrow so that you can meet him."

So the next day George braided his hair with extra care, and tied his cue up neatly with a fine black ribbon. He dressed himself in the new plum-colored suit and ruffled shirt which Lawrence had given him. And he put his large gold watch in his pocket.

Then he hung his long blue cape over his

shoulders. With his three-cornered hat under his arm he went outside, where Lawrence was waiting for him.

A stableboy was just leading two prancing horses to the doorstep. Lawrence mounted one. George mounted the other. Together the brothers set off down the road toward Belvoir.

It was a dreary winter afternoon. They found Lord Fairfax sitting in a big armchair before a crackling fire. He put down his book at once. After he had greeted Lawrence, he looked George over from head to foot.

"So this is your young brother, eh, Lawrence," he said. "If he's half as manly as he looks, I don't wonder you're proud of him."

He held out his hand to George. The boy bowed low as he shook it. He was surprised to find this great lord so friendly. He liked Lord Fairfax at once. And Lord Fairfax liked him.

Before the visit was over Lord Fairfax had asked George to go fox hunting with him the following morning. And the two had become good friends.

During the weeks that followed they went hunting together several times. George spent

*Together the brothers set off to see Lord Fairfax*

many hours at Belvoir. And Lord Fairfax came often to visit Lawrence and Anne at Mount Vernon. On these visits there was usually a great deal of talk about Lord Fairfax's land.

Most of this great tract was forest land. Here and there, a few brave settlers had made clearings and built log cabins. But the rest of the land had been left to Indians and wild animals.

One day Lord Fairfax announced that he was going to send a party of men to survey part of this forest land. He was having dinner at Mount Vernon when he spoke about this. And he looked down the long table, with its gleaming white cloth and shining silver, at Lawrence Washington.

"Anne's brother, young George Fairfax, is going with the party," he went on. "The head surveyor will be a man named Genn. Mr. Genn will hire all the chain-men and helpers he needs, but I wonder—"

He stopped speaking and looked across the table at George, who was listening intently. Then he looked back at Lawrence.

"I've seen some of the maps which George

[ *67* ]

has made of this part of the country," he said. "He takes great care with them, and they are always correct. What would you think of letting him join the party?"

Lawrence turned quickly to George. "Would you like to go?" he asked.

George choked down a mouthful of roast duck and nodded his head. He was almost too excited to speak. But he blurted out, "Yes, sir," with such joy that both men laughed.

"Splendid!" exclaimed Lord Fairfax. "Then you shall go."

So on Friday, March eleventh, in the year 1748, George rode off with young George Fairfax to meet the other surveyors. Lawrence and Anne stood on the steps to watch them go.

George waved good-by and settled himself in his saddle. His heart was pounding with excitement. He was off at last on a real adventure! He was going to help map out the wilderness which lay beyond the beautiful Blue Ridge Mountains.

# CHAPTER EIGHT

## *Into the Wilderness*

---

Rain TRICKLED from the brim of George's three-cornered hat. It soaked through his jacket. It ran in little rivers down the sleek neck and sides of his horse.

Through the curtain of rain he could see Mr. Fairfax and Mr. Genn, the head surveyor, riding along the trail ahead of him. He could hear the voices of the four assistant surveyors who were riding behind him. They talked in low tones as though they were tired.

George was tired, too. And wet and cold and hungry. But he was happy. He whistled softly as he jogged along under the dripping trees.

Twelve days had passed since he had left

Mount Vernon. Twelve days he thought he would never forget.

He had ridden for miles through deep forests. He had helped survey thousands of acres of land. He had climbed the Blue Ridge Mountains. He had forded rushing streams. He had swum his horse across the Potomac River when it was swift and swollen from spring rains.

[70]

He had learned to cook a meal on an outdoor fire. He had slept on the ground in a tent. And, in a settler's cabin, he had tried to sleep on a bed of straw which was alive with lice and fleas.

He smiled to think what his mother and Betty would say when he told them about that straw bed, the next time he visited Ferry Farm.

And his cousin Robin, at Chotank, would never believe how poor the settlers were. Nor how a settler's family had to live all crowded together in a tiny log cabin. A cabin with greasy paper instead of glass at the windows, and nothing but earth for the floor.

"I'm glad I brought along a book to keep a journal in," George thought. "I might forget some of the things that have happened if I didn't write them down."

He ducked his head as his horse walked under a low-hanging branch. Then he straightened up and gave a sigh of pleasure. They had come to the end of that day's journey. Already Mr. Genn had stopped his horse before a comfortable-looking log house.

"Here's Tom Cresap's," Mr. Genn called

back to George and the men. "Here's where we'll spend the night." He climbed from his saddle and knocked on the door.

Soon all the surveyors were warming their hands and drying their clothes in front of Tom Cresap's blazing fire. They were glad to be under a roof and out of the rain.

Roast wild turkey, fried ham, and hot corn-meal mush with molasses made a fine meal after a hard day's ride. When the meal was over the men lighted up their pipes. Then they sat down before the fire to talk with Mr. Cresap.

Mr. Thomas Cresap was a pioneer and an Indian trader. Part of his home was used as an Indian trading post. And he had many stories to tell about the red men who came to exchange skins and furs with him, for beads and knives and trinkets.

George listened to this talk with great interest. In all his sixteen years he had seen only two or three Indians. He did not know much about them. But he was soon to know more.

That night the surveyors rolled up in their blankets and lay down before the fire to sleep.

[72]

George could hear the rain beating down on the roof of the cabin. He hoped that it would stop before morning.

But it was still raining hard when he woke next day. It rained all that day and until the next day. Then it stopped.

All the surveyors were tired of waiting at the trading post for good weather. Now that the rain was over, they wanted to be on their way.

"Take a look outside, George, and see what the road is like," James Genn said. "If it's not too muddy for the horses, maybe we can start right off."

George nodded. He opened the door of the cabin. Then he gave a whistle of surprise.

"Hey, Mr. Cresap," he called excitedly. "Look here! You have visitors! Indians!"

Tom Cresap hurried to the door. The surveyors crowded close behind him. The clearing before the cabin was filled with Indian braves in war paint and feathers.

"There must be more than thirty of them out there," George Fairfax said in a low voice.

Mr. Genn nodded. "What are they up to,

*The clearing was filled with Indian braves in war paint and feathers*

Cresap?" he asked. "They don't look very friendly."

Tom Cresap laughed. "They're all good Indians," he said. "I know every one of them. Come on, and we'll find out what they want."

He went out to meet the Indians and the surveyors followed him. The redskins gathered around the white men quickly.

One of the Indians began to speak. He told Mr. Cresap that he and the other braves had been on the warpath against some Indians of another tribe.

"Me get scalp," he said, holding up a scalp by its long black hair. "Other braves get no scalp. Bad war."

He shivered as he spoke. George saw that some of the other Indians were also shivering. All of them looked cold and miserable.

"The poor fellows are freezing," James Genn said. "We'd better give them a bit of our rum to warm them up."

He went to the cabin and brought back a jug of rum. Then he opened it and passed some of the rum out to the red men.

The Indians drank it and grunted with pleasure.

"War dance!" one of the red men said to Mr. Genn. "You give firewater. We make war dance." And he began to talk to the other Indians in words that the surveyors could not understand.

The Indians started at once to gather wood and to build a huge fire in the clearing. It was nearly dark when they were ready to begin their war dance. But the fire burned brightly.

It lighted the copper-colored bodies of the Indians. And it made their knives and tomahawks gleam as they circled around the flames, leaping, running, jumping, and shouting their savage war cries.

George squatted on a log at the edge of the dark forest, watching everything with eager eyes. The dance ended all too soon for him. Then the Indians set about making camp in the clearing for the night. And the surveyors went back to the cabin.

Late that night, while the men were talking, George sat at a table, with a flickering candle at his elbow. Before him lay the copybook in which he was keeping his journal.

He dipped his quill pen into his leather ink bottle. With great care he began to write down an account of what had happened that day, and of how the Indians had danced.

"There manner of Dauncing is as follows," he wrote. "They clear a Large Circle and make a Great Fire in the middle. Then seats themselves around it. The Speaker makes a grand speech, telling them in what Manner they are to Daunce.

"After he has finished, the best Dauncer jumps up as one awaked out of a Sleep and Runs and Jumps about the ring in a most comicol Manner. He is followed by the Rest. Then begins there Musicians to play.

"The Musick is a Pot half of water with a Deerskin Stretched over it as tight as it can. And a goard with some Shott in it to Rattle. And a Piece of horses Tail tied to it to make it look fine. The one keeps Rattling and the other Drumming all the while the others is Dauncing."

George laid down his pen. There was nothing else he wanted to write about the Indians.

[77]

And the men were telling stories as they sat around the fire. Closing his journal, George put it in his knapsack. Then he sat down with the surveyors to listen to their talk.

Next day the Indians left Cresap's trading post. Soon the surveyors set out again on their journey. Day after day they pushed on to the northwest, making surveys along the way.

The weather was often bad. Twice, during stormy nights, their tent blew down. Once when they were all sleeping soundly, their bed of straw caught fire. But one man woke in time to save the others from being badly burned.

When their work was finished, the surveyors started home. Several days later, just as the sun was sinking, George pulled up his horse before the doorstep at Mount Vernon.

Lawrence and Anne were both delighted to see him. And the candles had burned low before he had told them all about his surveying trip. At last Lawrence rose from his chair. "You must be tired after riding all day," he said to George. "I think it's time we all went to bed."

[78]

George agreed sleepily. He said good night. Picking up his candle, he went upstairs.

How small his room looked after his journey into the wilderness! But it looked comfortable, too! He was glad to be back.

He was also glad to find that a servant had unpacked his knapsack. There on the table lay his journal beside his ink bottle and pen.

George picked the book up and looked through the pages. What a good time he had had on his journey over the mountains! And what a lot he had learned! About camping in the forest. About Indians. About how poor settlers lived. And, best of all, about surveying.

With a little smile, he picked up his pen. Dipping it in the ink, he wrote carefully:

"Wednesday the 13th of April 1748 Mr. Fairfax got safe home and I myself safe to my Brothers which concludes my Journal."

He blew on the words to dry the ink. Then he undressed quickly and put out his candle and went to bed.

[79]

# CHAPTER NINE

## *George Loses His Best Friend*

---

GEORGE KNOCKED some snow from his hat and brushed more snow from his long cape. Then he opened the door to the house at Ferry Farm and stepped into the wide hall.

A fire was burning brightly in the big fireplace, and the table was set for supper. But there was no one in sight.

George blew on his hands and held them out to the fire.

"Hey!" he shouted. "Is anybody home?"

"George! It's George!" Five voices called joyfully from different parts of the house.

Mrs. Washington's door at the end of the hall flew open and she bustled out in an instant. Jack and Charley and Sam raced pell-mell down the stairs. Betty came hurrying from her room, her skirts flying. And everyone gathered around George, talking at once.

Then Mrs. Washington and Betty each asked a question at the same moment.

"Are you hungry?"

"How long can you stay this time?"

George grinned. "I'm always hungry," he declared. "And I can stay two days. Then I must get back to Lawrence."

He unfastened his cape, with its gay red lining, and handed it to his youngest brother. "Here, Charley, please hang this up for me," he said. "Treat it with care, too, for it's new. I had it made right after I returned from my last surveying trip over the mountains."

Charles took the cape and looked at his brother with great respect. "Were you the head surveyor this time?" he asked.

George nodded. But before he could speak, his mother exclaimed, "Of course he was the head surveyor! Didn't he help lay out that new town called Alexandria? And now he's the surveyor for all of Culpeper County!"

She leaned over and patted George's arm.

[*81*]

"For a lad not yet eighteen, you've done very well, son," she went on. "I'm proud of you."

George's face reddened. "Lord Fairfax and Lawrence helped me get the position," he said.

"And your own good work helped, too,"

Betty added quickly. "Watch out, Charley, you're letting the cape touch the floor."

Charles lifted the cape higher and went to hang it up. Mrs. Washington sent Jack to tell the servant to lay another place at the table. Betty lighted the candles. And soon everyone was at supper.

It was a good meal, but George had to talk so much that he hardly had time to eat. Mrs. Washington wanted to hear all about Mount Vernon. Betty was curious about the big Christmas dance at Belvoir. And the boys had a dozen questions to ask about George's second trip to the wilderness beyond the mountains.

"Did you earn much money on this trip?" Sam asked.

"A doubloon a day," George replied.

Sam's mouth dropped open. "A doubloon a day!" he exclaimed. "That's a lot of money."

George nodded. He spread a hot biscuit with butter. "Sometimes I've earned more than that," he went on. "Of course I have to pay my helpers. But I have all the work I can do now. So I'm saving money all the time."

[ 83 ]

He bit into the biscuit and took a swallow of tea. "Soon I'll have money enough to buy some land," he said, setting down his cup. "Lawrence thinks that's a fine idea."

"How is Lawrence?" Mrs. Washington asked. "Is his cough better?"

"No," George replied soberly. "It's much worse. Anne's greatly worried about him, and so am I."

Indeed, George had good reason to be worried about his brother. When he returned to Mount Vernon from Ferry Farm, he found Lawrence coughing as badly as ever.

Poor Lawrence had already asked all the good doctors in Virginia about his cough. He had even been to England to talk to doctors there. But no one had been able to help him. He was growing paler and thinner every day.

At last he grew so ill that he decided to visit a warmer country. He hoped that a change of climate might help him. Anne wanted to go with him. But her new baby was not strong, and she could not leave the child.

"I'll go with Lawrence gladly," George offered.

So Anne said good-by to them with a heavy heart and off they sailed for the West Indies. But the trip did not help Lawrence. On a hot July day, soon after his return home, he died.

George could never forget that day. It seemed that the light had suddenly gone out of the world. Lawrence had been more to him than a brother. He had been like a father to him. He had been his best friend, too.

Alone in his room, young George Washington could not hold back his tears. Mount Vernon would never be the same to him again.

Anne went to live with her father at Belvoir, which was not far away. And George was now the master of Mount Vernon.

# CHAPTER TEN

# Bad News from Beyond the Mountains

---

IT WAS a warm evening in February. A servant opened a window in the library at Belvoir for a minute to let some fresh air into the room. The candles in their heavy silver holders flickered, and one of them went out.

Mr. George Fairfax lighted it again. Then he turned to a tall young man in a new blue uniform, who sat near him in a big armchair.

"So you're a major in the Virginia Militia, eh, George?" he asked. "Congratulations!"

"Thank you," George Washington replied. "Lawrence arranged it for me, you know. He asked Governor Dinwiddie to make me an officer in the militia, before he died."

Mr. Fairfax smiled. He knew that there were other reasons why George was now a major.

"You're young to be an officer," he said.

"But you have a good head on your shoulders."

George looked pleased. He crossed one long leg over the other. "I'm not sure just what a major's duties are," he said gravely. "But I bought some books in Williamsburg after I had talked with the Governor. Books on drilling soldiers and fighting battles. I shall study them carefully."

Mr. Fairfax nodded. "You may soon need to know all that they can teach you," he declared. "It looks to me as though we were going to have trouble with the French. I hear they're building a fort near Lake Erie. And a few of them have pushed south from Canada, right into the Ohio country."

George leaned forward in his chair. "The Ohio country!" he exclaimed hotly. "That land belongs to us."

Mr. Fairfax laughed. "The French don't think so," he said, knocking some tobacco from his thin clay pipe. "They claim that all the land west of the Allegheny Mountains is theirs. And we claim it's ours. That's why there'll be trouble. When it comes, you—"

[ 87 ]

*"So you're a major in the Virginia Militia, eh, George?"*
*asked Mr. Fairfax*

He broke off suddenly. "Ah, here's Sally!" he exclaimed.

And there was his lovely young wife at the door. Both men sprang to their feet as she entered. There was no more talk that evening of French soldiers or the Ohio country.

Indeed, it was some time before George Washington thought of the Ohio country again. For he was now a very busy young man.

He studied his books on war and managed Mount Vernon. He made many surveys. He went fox hunting with his friends from Belvoir and other plantations. He played whist and loo and billiards. And he danced the minuet with pretty girls from many miles around.

Meanwhile, in the forests near the Ohio River, strange things were happening. Governor Dinwiddie in Williamsburg was hearing stories that made him angry and worried.

Trappers sent word to him from the Ohio country that French soldiers had robbed them of their furs and pack horses. A trader galloped into Williamsburg to say that he had been thrown out of his trading post by the French.

Two other traders had been killed. Indians who had been friendly to settlers from Virginia were now friendly with the French.

All this was bad news for the Governor of Virginia. For Virginia was one of the thirteen American colonies which belonged to England. And Governor Dinwiddie had been sent by the English king to govern it.

What would that king say if French soldiers were allowed to take over good rich land which England claimed?

With a worried frown the Governor sat down one day and wrote to England, asking what he had better do. Two months later, back came an answer from the King himself.

"Build forts in the Ohio country," the King commanded. "Send soldiers from your colony to defend the forts. Drive the French out of my land even if you have to fight them. But before you do any of these things, send a letter to the commander of the French and ask him to leave the country peacefully."

It did not take Governor Dinwiddie long to write that letter. As soon as it was finished he hired two men and told them to search the Ohio country until they had found the commander of the French fort near Lake Erie.

The men set off at once. But before long they were both back in Williamsburg.

"Travel is now very dangerous in the wilderness," they said. "Many Indians are siding with the French. We were not able to get to the French fort. Here, sir, is your letter back again."

Now Governor Dinwiddie knew he must

find another messenger. Someone braver and stronger and more determined than these men.

He was thinking about this as he sat at his desk one fine October day. And he looked up impatiently when a servant announced that someone wished to see him. But his face brightened when his visitor appeared.

"Ah, Major Washington!" he exclaimed. "Come in. What brings you here?"

"I have a favor to ask of you, sir," George Washington said, stepping close to the desk.

"Friends have told me that you are having trouble getting a letter delivered to the French commander in the Ohio country. Will you allow me to deliver that letter for you?"

"Do you think you can?" Governor Dinwiddie asked quickly.

"I'd like to try, sir," George replied soberly.

Governor Dinwiddie leaned back in his chair. For a moment he stared thoughtfully at George Washington. Then he nodded his head. "You have courage, Major Washington," he said. "Sit down and we'll make plans at once for your journey."

[92]

# CHAPTER ELEVEN

## A Dangerous Errand

---

IT WAS a cold November night. Wind swept down the swift-flowing Allegheny River. It howled through the trees growing thick along the banks of the river. It blew fiercely against the tent pitched on the shore, making the sides billow and flap.

Inside the tent, George Washington shivered and pulled his blanket more closely around his neck. He could not sleep. But it was not the wind which was keeping him awake. Nor the snores of the six men lying near him. It was his own thoughts.

Nearly a month had passed since he had talked with Governor Dinwiddie in Williamsburg. But he remembered well the orders which the Governor had given him.

[93]

"Hire men to help you and buy whatever supplies you will need," the Governor had said. "Then set out at once for the Indian village called Logstown, on the Ohio River. The Indians in Logstown are still friendly to us. Their chief is named Half King.

"Ask Half King to help you find the French commander. While you are waiting for the commander's reply to my letter, find out all that you can about the French. How many soldiers they have. How they are armed. And what kind of forts they have built. Then return as quickly as you can to Williamsburg. Waste no time on your journey."

George smiled in the dark when he thought of those last words. He hadn't wasted a minute!

Since leaving Williamsburg he had bought a tent, compasses, guns, ammunition, blankets, and presents for the Indians. Medicines, food, horses and corn to feed them, as well as a deerskin suit for himself.

He had hired a man who could speak French and a famous guide named Christopher Gist.

He had also hired four other men who had traded with the Indians of the Ohio country and knew their language.

With this party of men he had pushed more than a hundred miles through deep forests, over snowy mountains, and across rushing rivers. He had passed the Forks of the Ohio— that place where the Allegheny and Mononga- hela Rivers come together. Then he had crossed the Allegheny.

"Tomorrow we will get to Logstown," he thought. And he began to plan what he would say to the Indians when he asked their help in finding the French commander.

Early the next day Major Washington and his party started off for Logstown. The sun had set before they rode into the little village of Indian huts.

Dogs ran out to bark at them. Black-eyed children stared shyly from the doorways of the smoky huts. A tall Indian came from the big- gest hut to ask what the white men wanted.

One of Major Washington's men who knew the Indian's language leaned from his saddle.

[95]

"Where is your chief, Half King?" he asked.

"Not here now," the Indian replied. "He will come tomorrow. Pitch your tent and stay."

So the white men tethered their horses and pitched their tent. The next day Half King arrived at Logstown. George went at once to call on the great chief in his cabin. He told Half King why he had come. And he asked his help in finding the French commander.

Half King listened gravely. The English were his friends. He did not like the French.

"I was in French fort," he said. "I talk with

[*96*]

French chief. I say, 'Go from our country. You don't go, we fight you.' "

"What was his answer to that?" George asked eagerly.

Half King's eyes flashed with anger. "He say Indians are like flies and mosquitoes to French. French not afraid."

Then Half King went on to tell George that the French fort was many, many miles to the north. "You wait," he said. "Maybe I go. Show you way. Maybe I take men to help fight if you meet bad Indians."

"Maybe!" George thought impatiently. But this was too good a chance to lose. So he hid his impatience and waited.

For five days he waited for Half King to make up his mind. He visited with the Indians. He gave them presents. He listened to them make long speeches. He even made a speech himself. Standing up in the dark, smoky long house, he spoke to all the important men of Half King's tribe, and asked them to help him get to the French fort.

At last Half King decided that he and three other Indians would go with George and his party. They set out at once through the forest. Twelve days later they reached Fort LeBeouf, near Lake Erie.

The French commander received them politely. He smiled when he read the letter which Governor Dinwiddie had sent to him. And he made ready to write a polite reply.

George knew what that reply would be. So did his scout, Christopher Gist.

"The French won't leave," Gist said to Major Washington. "It looks to me like they are going to take all the Ohio country, even if they have to fight for it."

George nodded. He had already examined the big fort, with its cannon and its high stockade. He had seen the great fleet of canoes which the French had built to take them down the Ohio River. Everything he saw told him that the French were getting ready to make war.

"I must get back to Williamsburg quickly to warn the Governor," he thought.

He was soon given the French commander's

*George had already examined the big French fort*

reply to the Governor's letter. Carefully he put it in a deerskin packet with notes and maps that he had made of his journey. Then he gathered his men and the Indians together and started back.

After they had traveled toward the south for several days, Half King and the other Indians left the party. George and his men pushed on alone through the wilderness.

It was December now and bitter cold. The snow was deep. The trails were hard to find. The wind was biting. But for ten days they struggled on. Then the horses became too tired to go any farther. And three of the men were so badly frostbitten that they could barely move.

"We'll have to build a camp where these men and horses can wait until the weather is warmer," George said to Christopher Gist. "You and I can go ahead on foot to the nearest settlement where we can get horses."

Gist shook his head. He knew that George Washington was used to riding horseback and had seldom walked for any long distance

[100]

through the woods. "Don't try it, Major," he begged. "Don't try it. You'd never be able to make such a trip on foot."

"I must make it, Gist," George replied earnestly. "I don't dare to lose one day in getting back to Williamsburg."

So they quickly built a shelter for the frost-bitten men. Then George and Christopher Gist set out alone toward the southeast.

With packs on their backs and guns in their hands, they plunged through snowdrifts, up hill and down. Mile after mile they traveled, until every bone in Washington's body ached and his legs would carry him no farther. For

[*101*]

a while they rested. Then they started off again.

All that day and the next they pushed ahead. They were trying to reach the Allegheny River. For Gist knew that there was a trading post beyond the river, where they could get horses.

"We won't have any trouble getting across the river," Gist said as they tramped on through the snow. "That old Allegheny will be frozen solid from shore to shore."

But Gist was wrong. When he and George reached the river they found it only partly frozen. In midstream the open water rushed along swiftly, carrying with it huge pieces of ice.

George whistled under his breath. "There's only one way we can get to the other shore," he said. "That's on a raft. Get out your hatchet, Gist."

Gist nodded and began to unfasten his pack. Then he and George went to work. All day long they took turns with the hatchet, chopping down trees. They bound the trees together with wild grapevines and each man cut himself a long stout pole.

It was nearly dark when they pushed the raft across the ice to the open water. They launched it carefully. Then they climbed aboard.

In an instant the angry river caught the raft and swirled it around. Great blocks of ice bumped against it, tossing it this way and that. George put his pole down into the water and pushed on it with all his weight, to hold the raft steady.

But the current was too strong. The raft hit the pole. Suddenly George was hurled into the river. And the black icy water closed over his head.

He came up sputtering and coughing, just as the raft swept past him. Quickly he grabbed at one of the logs and pulled himself aboard again. His clothes were already beginning to freeze on his body. He had lost his pole.

The men could not manage the raft with only one pole.

"See that island," Gist shouted above the

roar of the river. "The water is shallow there. When we pass it, grab your gun and wade ashore."

George nodded. As the raft came abreast of the island both men leaped into the water and splashed ashore. And there, on that tiny island, with the icy wind howling around them, they spent the night.

It was a horrible night. The two men nearly froze to death before it was over. But they managed to keep awake by moving around. When daylight came at last, they made a joyful discovery. Solid ice lay between the island and the east shore of the river. They crossed it quickly and made for the trading post, which was five miles away.

There, before a blazing fire, George opened the deerskin packet which held his papers. His fingers were still stiff from the cold. But he pulled out the precious letter from the French commander and looked it over carefully. Not a drop of water had touched it! It was clean and dry!

Twelve days later George Washington galloped into Williamsburg and laid that letter on Governor Dinwiddie's desk.

But his work was not yet over. For the Governor wanted a written report of everything he had done and seen and heard.

When that report was finished, the Governor had it printed. He was now sure that there would be war with the French. So he sent copies of George's report to other American colonies, asking them for help. He sent copies to England, too.

Soon the men who read these reports were asking themselves, "Who is this young man— George Washington?"

# CHAPTER TWELVE

## *Washington Is Left Behind*

---

IT WAS a beautiful day in April more than a year later. But it didn't seem like a beautiful day to Mrs. Washington. When her two-wheeled carriage stopped before the house at Mount Vernon, she stepped out at once. Then she lifted the knocker on the front door and let it fall with a bang.

George himself answered the knock.

"Mother!" he exclaimed. "What a pleasant surprise! Come in."

He stooped to kiss his mother, but she pushed him away and walked past him into the hall. When she turned to face him there were tears in her eyes.

"George, I will not let you do it!" she said. "I know General Braddock has asked you to be his aide-de-camp. But I will not let you go to war again."

"Let me!" George repeated in amazement. "But, Mother, I'm a soldier. I—"

"Yes," Mrs. Washington broke in. "You're a soldier. And look what happened to you when you went out against the French!"

George's face flushed. He did not like to be reminded of his battle with the French. He remembered all too well just what had happened.

He had delivered the letter from the French commander to Governor Dinwiddie. He had written a long report of his journey. Then the Governor had put him in command of a small troop of soldiers.

"Men from this colony are already building a fort at the Forks of the Ohio," the Governor had said. "March your soldiers to the Forks. Help finish the fort and stay to defend it."

George and his soldiers had set out at once for the fort. But before they could reach it the French had captured it, and named it Fort Duquesne.

[*107*]

When he heard this news George had decided that he must build another fort at once. He had studied his books on war. But none of them had told him what to do at a time like this. And he built his fort in an open meadow, surrounded by hills.

It was hardly finished when a large force of French and Indians attacked it. They shot from behind the bushes and trees on the hills around the meadow. After a hard fight, they captured the fort. George and his men had returned sadly to Virginia, defeated.

Young George Washington had made a great mistake in choosing that place for his fort. But he had done the very best he could. He had fought bravely, too. Now he had been asked to start off for the Forks of the Ohio again.

He was a grown man, eager to fight for his king and his country. And here was his mother, talking to him as if he were a little boy. Telling him that he must stay home and keep out of danger.

He clenched his fists and choked back the

angry words that sprang to his lips. It was only because she loved him that she wanted to keep him out of danger. And he knew it. So he put his strong arm around her shoulders and led her into the sitting room. There he tried to laugh away her fears.

Within a few days he was galloping off to meet General Braddock's army, which had just come from England.

It was a splendid-looking army. The English soldiers wore gay scarlet uniforms. Their bayonets were shining. When the drums beat loudly and the trumpets called, they fell promptly into line. Off they marched proudly toward the country beyond the mountains.

They were going to take back the fort at the Forks of the Ohio which the French had captured! They were going to drive the French soldiers from the Ohio country forever!

General Braddock set out on the journey in a fine carriage. George and two other aides trotted behind him on prancing horses.

After they had ridden almost all day, one of the English aides looked at George in dismay.

[ *109* ]

"This wilderness!" he exclaimed. "We have nothing like it in England. Does it go on forever?"

George laughed. He knew something about the wilderness. "It goes on for thousands of miles, Captain Orme," he replied. "You can ride for weeks and still be in the forest."

"But what about roads?" Captain Orme asked, looking ahead at the general's carriage.

"There aren't any," George replied, with a twinkle in his eyes. "When we reach the end of this one, the men will have to build more."

He smiled. He liked Captain Orme. He liked General Braddock, too. And the English general already had a high opinion of George. Soon he and young Colonel Washington had become good friends.

Often they talked together about the Ohio country. Sometimes the general even asked Washington for advice. But he did not always take it.

"Our greatest danger will be from Indians who are friendly to the French," George said one day.

[*110*]

The general laughed. "Perhaps soldiers from Virginia find the Indians dangerous," he said. "But those poor savages could never harm *my* army." Suddenly he looked sharply at George. "My dear boy!" he exclaimed. "You look ill."

George put his hand to his head. "It's nothing but a headache, sir, and a little fever," he said quickly. "They'll soon leave me."

But they didn't. The next day George was worse. Yet he insisted on going ahead with

[ *111* ]

the army. For he wanted very much to be with General Braddock when the attack was made on Fort Duquesne. Day after day he traveled, lying uncomfortably in a wagon that bumped and jolted over the rough road.

At last he became so ill that General Braddock told him that he could not go on. He commanded him to stay behind and to rest until he was well.

So poor George went to bed in a tent, with a man to take care of him. And there he lay while the army marched on without him.

# CHAPTER THIRTEEN

## A Dreadful Day

---

GENERAL BRADDOCK'S army was a big army. It moved slowly. Day after day it wound its way over the mountains and through the leafy forests, like a great snake nearly four miles long.

Road builders went ahead, chopping down trees and clearing away brush. Wagons bumped along at the rear, carrying supplies and ammunition.

These wagons were driven by men from Virginia and near-by colonies. One of the wagoners was a tall young man from the Yadkin valley in North Carolina. He was the best hunter and trapper in all the colony. And his name was Daniel Boone.

[*113*]

In his tent by the roadside, George Washington tossed on his bed and listened to the wagons go rumbling by. Every day he swallowed the bitter powders which General Braddock himself had ordered him to take. And

Daniel Boone

he did his best to get well. For he was still determined to catch up with the army before it reached Fort Duquesne.

As soon as he was strong enough to get out of bed, he sent for a wagon and a man to drive it. Then he set out at once to overtake General Braddock.

One evening more than two weeks later, he reached the place where General Braddock had made camp for the night. Captain Orme came hurrying from one of the tents to help George from the wagon.

"Gad, but you're thin!" he exclaimed to his friend. "The general plans to attack the fort tomorrow. But you'll never be able to sit on a horse. Your bones will come right through your skin."

George laughed. "They won't if I put a pillow on my saddle," he declared. And that is what he did.

Early the next morning the general and his army set off to attack the fort. By midafternoon they had almost reached it. Not an Indian or a Frenchman had appeared to block their way.

In their bright scarlet uniforms, the men marched steadily forward through the woods. Birds chirped in the branches over their heads. Rabbits scurried out of their way.

Suddenly the forest was filled with horrible Indian war cries. Bullets rained on the English soldiers. Many of them dropped to the ground, dead or wounded. Others raised their muskets to fire.

But what could they shoot at? Where was their enemy?

Their enemy was everywhere! Hidden in the underbrush! Crawling in the grass! Crouching behind rocks! Shooting from the trees! And above the sound of gunfire, terrible Indian war whoops rang out again and again.

For a while the English soldiers stood their ground bravely. Bravely they tried to fight a foe they could not see. Then they broke ranks and ran in wild disorder.

General Braddock and his officers rode among them, waving their swords and shouting orders. Washington galloped here and there, trying to rally the terrified men.

Suddenly his horse screamed with pain and dropped to the ground. As the animal fell, George leaped from the saddle. The woods were now full of riderless horses. He caught one and mounted quickly.

A bullet tore through his hat. Another ripped his sleeve. His second horse was killed.

*Their enemy was everywhere! Hidden in the underbrush . . . behind rocks!*

He mounted a third. More bullets whizzed past his ears. The third horse fell. But he found a fourth.

"Fight!" he shouted to the fleeing soldiers. "Come on, men! Fight! Fight! Fight!"

Some of the men did. But most of the soldiers ran. For they had been trained to fight on battlefields and not in forests where an enemy lurked behind every tree.

When night came the woods were filled with dead and dying men. General Braddock had been so badly wounded that he died within a few days. And Fort Duquesne still belonged to the French.

Two of General Braddock's aides had been badly wounded in the battle. Washington arranged to have them taken to places of safety, where they could be cared for.

Sorrowfully he ordered some soldiers to dig a grave in the road for General Braddock. When the general had been buried, George asked wagoners to drive their wagons over the mound of earth. For he wanted to hide the grave forever from the French and their Indian friends.

There were many other things to be done. And it was several days before he could stop work and go home to rest. By that time men

*General Braddock*

in Virginia were saying fine things about young Washington. So were men in other colonies.

"There's a steady young man," they told one another. "So ill he could hardly sit in a saddle! Three horses shot right out from under him! Yet he never gave up."

[*119*]

"He's a brave one, all right! What's more, he knows how to keep his head in time of danger. He's the kind of man this country needs."

Governor Dinwiddie certainly needed Washington. For now more Indians were taking sides with the French. They were already beginning to attack the little settlements on the Virginia frontier. So the Governor made George Washington the commander in chief of all the soldiers in Virginia. And he sent Colonel Washington out to protect the settlers.

Two years later another general was sent from England to try to capture Fort Duquesne. Off marched Colonel Washington and his men to help him.

But when they reached the Forks of the Ohio they found that they did not need to fight. The French had learned that they were coming. They had set fire to the fort and fled to the north. They had left the Ohio country forever.

How glad Washington was to march his

*"Fight!"* he shouted to the fleeing soldiers. *"Come on, men! Fight! Fight!"*

troops back to Virginia! How good it was to get home to Mount Vernon!

He took off his uniform and gave it to a servant to put away. He was through with war. He hoped that he would never have to be a soldier again.

He had fallen in love with a pretty, rich, young widow named Martha Custis, who had two little children. She loved him, too. And he was going to marry her as soon as he could. Then he planned to settle down at Mount Vernon, and to live there for the rest of his life.

# CHAPTER FOURTEEN

## *Happy Years*

---

I T WAS seven o'clock on a fine spring morning, eighteen months later. The sun shone
down on Mount Vernon. It made the newly
painted house gleam as white as snow.

Jacky Custis opened the door. He stepped
outside. So did his little sister, Patsy. For a
moment the two children stood in the doorway looking all around. Suddenly Jacky
darted down the steps. He ran across the grass
toward the stable. Patsy followed closely at his
heels.

"Papa!" Jacky shouted. "Papa! You didn't
wait for us. You ate your breakfast without
us."

George Washington was standing near the
stable door, talking to two young Negroes. He

turned when he heard Jacky call and held out his arms. A minute later he swung the little boy off his feet and lifted him high over his head. Then he set him down and caught Patsy to him with a hug.

Jacky was breathless. He looked soberly at his stepfather. "Patsy and I had to eat our hoe cakes and honey without you," he said. "You didn't wait."

Colonel Washington laughed. "I couldn't wait this morning, Jacky," he said. "I have too many things to do."

"What things?" Patsy asked.

Colonel Washington ruffled her dark hair. "Well," he said, "I must see about planting some pear trees. And give orders to have two hogsheads of tobacco sent to Alexandria. And select some lambs to be—"

He broke off suddenly. "Look, here's Billy, bringing my horse from the stable. I must go. Run to your nurse now, and I'll see you at dinnertime."

He watched the children scamper across the grass. Then he took the reins from the stable-

*He had become a farmer and he was determined to be a good one*

boy and swung himself into the saddle. And he rode slowly down the driveway.

The spring air was soft and sweet. A mockingbird sang joyfully in one of the tall trees near the house. Colonel Washington smiled to himself as he jogged along.

He had been happy since he married Martha Custis. He had been very busy, too. For he had become a farmer and he was determined to be a good one.

Nearly every day he rode around his big plantation to make sure that things were going well. He talked with the men working in the fields about the way the tobacco and wheat and corn were growing. He kept a sharp eye on his herd of cows and his fine sheep and his oxen and his horses.

He made experiments with different kinds of seeds. He grafted fruit trees. He kept a careful record of all these things. And he studied every book he could get, on farming.

One gray fall afternoon he sat in his study reading a book about the care of cattle. Patsy was sitting on his lap with her doll in her arms.

Jacky was on the floor at his feet, looking at a storybook which had just come from England.

Suddenly Martha Washington appeared in the doorway. She laughed when she saw her husband.

"How can you do any reading that way?" she asked. "The children should be with their nurse and you should be dressing, my dear. I've ordered the coach for five o'clock. And Cully is upstairs now, laying out your clothes."

Colonel Washington slid Patsy from his knee and stood up. He had forgotten that he and his wife were going to a ball that evening. He was very fond of dancing. With a smile for Martha, he hurried upstairs to change his clothes.

By candle-lighting time he and Mrs. Washington were dressed and the coach was at the door. Jacky and Patsy came into the hall to say good-by.

How fine their stepfather looked in his light-blue suit and embroidered satin vest! The gold buckles on his knee breeches gleamed. So did the buckles on his low black

[ 127 ]

shoes. His hair had been nicely powdered and his cue was tucked into a fine silk bag.

The children watched him as he held a cloak for their mother to put over her dress of gay flowered silk. Then Washington wrapped himself in a cape and picked up his three-cornered hat.

He helped his wife into the coach. And they were off. The ball was a splendid affair and the evening passed swiftly.

Indeed, the years passed swiftly for George and Martha Washington. It seemed almost no time at all before Jack was old enough to go duck shooting and fox hunting with his step-father. Patsy was taking music lessons on the spinet. And Washington had hired a dancing teacher for both the children.

Sometimes Colonel Washington and his wife took the children to the theater in Alexandria, which was only eight miles away. And once in a great while they all went together in the big coach to Williamsburg.

But it was a four-day journey to the capital of the colony. And Patsy was not a strong child.

*He helped his wife into the coach. And they were off*

So when Washington went to Williamsburg, he usually went alone.

Jack and Patsy always hated to see him leave.

"Don't go," Patsy begged one day, when she saw him making ready for the journey.

"I must go, Patsy," her stepfather said, smoothing her dark hair back from her face. "The House of Burgesses is having a meeting. And I'm a member of the House. So I have to be there."

"What do you do?" Patsy asked.

"Help make the laws that govern all of us who live here in Virginia," Washington replied. "Go and practice your music lesson now, and I'll bring you a present when I come back."

So Patsy went to practice her music lesson. And soon George Washington set out for Williamsburg. When he came home many days later he brought presents for everyone. But he seemed tired and worried.

There were guests for dinner that day. And it was late in the evening before Mrs. Washington had a chance to talk with her husband alone.

Washington was seated at his desk. His journal lay open before him. He had his quill pen in his hand. But he was not writing.

Mrs. Washington picked up her knitting and sat down in a chair beside him.

"What happened in Williamsburg, George?" she asked. "What makes you look so worried?"

George Washington laid down his pen and swung around in his chair.

"It's these new taxes on things we must buy from England!" he exclaimed. "Taxes on paper, glass, paint, tea—"

He broke off suddenly and shook his head. "It's a great pity that George the Third is not a wise king like his father. He's treating us all so badly that not many of us will put up with it much longer."

Mrs. Washington laid her knitting in her lap. "What do you mean?" she asked in a puzzled voice. "Surely you don't mean there will be war?"

"I hope not," George Washington answered gravely. "But if war comes I shall—"

He looked up quickly. "There's Patsy calling!" he exclaimed. And he jumped to his feet.

Poor Patsy had never been really well. Often she suddenly became very ill and needed help.

Picking up a candle in its tall glass chimney, Colonel Washington ran up the stairs, two at a time. Mrs. Washington dropped her knitting to the floor and hurried after him.

For a while they were both busy taking care of Patsy. By the time she was comfortable again, King George and the new taxes had been forgotten, for that night at least.

# CHAPTER FIFTEEN

## *"We'll Fight for Our Rights"*

---

IT WAS the first day of September, 1774. No breeze came from the Potomac River. And it seemed that every room in the house was hot.

Mrs. Washington fanned herself with her handkerchief. She looked at the paper in her hand. Then she spoke to the servant who was laying out clothes on the big four-poster bed.

"And ten ruffled shirts, Cully," she said. "Pack them well so that they won't be wrinkled when the colonel gets to Philadelphia."

"Yes, ma'am," the servant replied.

"That's all," said Mrs. Washington. And she went downstairs in search of her husband. She found him outdoors. He was talking to one of the carpenters who were building an extra room on one side of the house.

[*133*]

George Washington smiled when he saw his wife.

"Think how fine this will be when it's finished," he said. "Some day we'll have a portico all the way across the front, where we can sit in the shade and watch the river."

Mrs. Washington nodded. She put her arm through her husband's and led him around the house.

"George, you'll come back as soon as you can, won't you?" she asked.

Washington covered his wife's plump little hand with his big one. He knew how lonely she would be while he was gone. For Jack was married now and dark-eyed Patsy had died suddenly several months earlier.

"Yes," he promised. "I'll come home as soon as the Congress ends."

He had no idea how soon that would be. And neither had anyone else.

The people in the American colonies were still having trouble with their king. George the Third did not understand his American subjects. He had made many foolish laws for them. And there were still heavy taxes on many things brought from England.

"As long as those things are so heavily taxed, we won't buy them," the colonists announced.

"Oh, yes, you will," insisted King George and the English government.

And one cold December day three English ships sailed into Boston harbor, loaded with tea. Tea with a tax on it!

"We won't even let that tea be unloaded here," many people in Boston declared.

That evening a number of Boston men disguised themselves as Indians. After dark they

[*135*]

crept aboard the boats and threw the tea into the water.

News of this Boston tea party soon reached George the Third. It made him very angry. He commanded the people of Boston to close their harbor until the tea had been paid for. Then he sent red-coated soldiers across the ocean to see that his orders were carried out.

This was a terrible punishment. With their harbor closed, many people in Massachusetts could not make a living.

There was trouble with the English government in other colonies, also. And the colonists decided at last that they must band together to help one another. Each colony chose a few of its most important men to go to a meeting in Philadelphia to talk things over.

George Washington was one of the men chosen by the colony of Virginia. So he said good-by to Martha on a hot September day in 1774. And he set out for Philadelphia to take part in the First Continental Congress.

Nearly two months passed before he came home again, tired and dusty after his four-day

*So he said good-by to Martha on a hot September
day in 1774*

journey. That night at the dinner table he told Mrs. Washington all that had happened at Philadelphia.

"And so we decided to send a letter to the King," he said as he ended his story. "We have asked him to treat us all with more justice and understanding. In May the Congress will meet again to discuss his reply."

Mrs. Washington took a spoonful of jelly from a plate which a servant held before her.

"What will happen if the King sends no reply?" she asked.

George Washington's eyes flashed. "Then we'll fight for our rights," he said quietly. "We should begin to get ready at once."

Many men in the colonies felt as Washington did—that they should prepare for war. Companies of soldiers were quickly formed in Virginia. And Washington was asked to take command of them.

Winter passed. Still no word came from the King. Then, in April, something happened near Boston which startled everyone in the colonies. Men on horseback galloped night and day to carry the news.

"Fighting has begun!" they shouted, pulling their horses up in little towns and villages. "Fighting has begun!"

They told the people who gathered around them that there had been a battle near Boston. A battle over gunpowder which English soldiers had tried to take from the colonists.

Ninety-three Americans had been killed. Two hundred and ninety-three English soldiers would never march again. And the rest of the English soldiers were shut up in Boston, surrounded by an army of angry men.

This was bad news indeed. George Washington's face was grave as he made ready in May to go to the second meeting of the Congress in Philadelphia. Since he was in command of the Virginia troops, he put on his uniform of blue and tan.

He was so tall and straight and handsome that Mrs. Washington smiled proudly when she saw him. But a moment later her eyes filled with tears. She brushed them away quickly.

"Take care of yourself, George," she said, catching hold of his coat button. "Come back safely. And write to me while you're away."

Washington nodded and stooped to kiss her good-by. "I'll send you a letter by the first post," he promised. "And I'll be home as soon as I can. I'd rather be here at Mount Vernon with you than anywhere else in the world."

He gave her a quick hug and went outside. A moment later he had mounted his horse. With a servant in bright red livery on a horse behind him, he trotted down the drive.

He did not guess, as he rode away from Mount Vernon, how many years would pass before he would see his home again.

# CHAPTER SIXTEEN

## *King George Takes a Tumble*

---

IT WAS a fine June day. In an open square in Philadephia a parade was forming. Soldiers on horseback moved their restless animals into line. Carriages filled with men in knee breeches and three-cornered hats lined up.

Drummers tightened the heavy drums hanging around their necks. Trumpeters made ready to play. At last the music began with a flourish. And the parade started off.

People dropped their work and leaned from their windows. They crowded to their doorways. They hurried to the street to watch the parade pass. And everyone talked to everyone else about the tall man at the head of the procession, who rode on the high-stepping horse.

"There he is! General Washington!"

[*141*]

*Everyone talked about the tall man at the head
of the procession*

"My, ain't he big!"

"Where's he going? What's he going to do?"

"He's going to Boston to chase the redcoats out."

"How far is the parade going with him?"

"Not far. They'll turn around and come back soon."

"Look at him. He's lifting his hat!"

"Law! Don't he look solemn?"

So the people talked, as the parade made its way through the narrow street.

George Washington, riding on his big horse, had very good reason to look solemn. The colonists were now ready to fight for their right to make their own laws and set their own taxes. Some men were even talking excitedly about breaking away from England. About freedom and independence.

Everyone was certain that there would now be a war. And George Washington had been chosen by every member of the Second Continental Congress to be the Commander in Chief of the American Army.

But there was no real army yet. Washington

knew that men must be enlisted from every colony. That uniforms must be found for them. And food, and guns, and ammunition. That they must be drilled to fight the well-trained English soldiers. And that every red-coat must be driven from the land.

It was a tremendous task for any man. Washington wasn't sure that he could carry it out. He needed time to think and plan. He was glad when the parade turned back. Then he and a small group of his officers rode on alone.

Many days later they reached the camp outside of Boston. Already there had been another terrible battle there, at a place called Bunker Hill. The redcoats had captured the hill. The war had really begun.

Washington's heart sank when he saw the colonists who had been fighting the British. They were farmers, blacksmiths, shopkeepers, clerks, and scholars. Brave men, all. But not an army! He went to work at once to make them into one.

Month after month Washington's army grew stronger. When spring came he told his men that he planned to make a surprise attack on the English soldiers in Boston.

One dark night he ordered his men to drag cannon, guns, and boxes of ammunition to the top of two hills near the city. All night the men worked, hardly making a sound.

Dawn came. Quietly, Washington gave the command to attack. Guns blazed! Cannon roared! The people in Boston jumped from their beds. Startled redcoats ran to the streets. For a while they tried to fight back. Then they scrambled aboard English ships and sailed away.

How the people in Boston cheered when the American Army marched into their little city! But Washington did not stay long in Boston.

Ships were already crossing the ocean bound for America, loaded with English soldiers. Congress ordered him to march his army to New York to defend that city.

Meanwhile the men in the Congress in Philadelphia had been trying to raise money and to make plans for the Army. Now those men decided that the time had come to tell the world that Americans were tired of being ruled by England. That they did not intend to be ruled by any country. That they were a free nation, able to govern themselves.

Benjamin Franklin, Thomas Jefferson, and three other men in the Congress were asked to plan this declaration. Together they decided what they wanted to say. Then Thomas Jefferson wrote it down in his own words. It was called a "Declaration of Independence."

Copies of the Declaration of Independence were printed at once. And messengers left Philadelphia to carry them to all the colonies.

One hot July afternoon Washington sat in his headquarters in New York. He was talking over plans with some of his officers. Birds chirped softly in the trees just outside the open window. And everything was very quiet.

Suddenly from the street there came the sound of shouting and cheering. Washington and his officers sprang to their feet. At that moment an aide burst through the door.

"It's come, Your Excellency! It's come!" he exclaimed excitedly. And he thrust a paper into Washington's outstretched hand.

*Washington's eyes shone as he unfolded the paper.*
*It was dated July 4, 1776*

Washington's eyes shone as he broke the seal and unfolded the paper. It was dated July 4, 1776. Quickly his eyes traveled down the page. He had known for some time that this was coming. But how brave the words looked in print!

" 'We solemnly publish and declare,' " he read aloud, " 'that the United Colonies are free and independent states.' "

He looked at his officers. "The United States of America!" he exclaimed. "How fine that sounds!"

"And we're free!" young Colonel Mifflin cried excitedly. "Free of England at last!"

Washington shook his head. "Not yet, Colonel," he declared. "Two enemy ships are anchored right now in the Hudson River. The enemy camp in Staten Island is filled with soldiers. And every week brings more to our shores. No, we're not free yet. But we'll fight for freedom until, with God's help, we win it."

He turned to his secretary. "Please make copies of this Declaration at once. I will have it read to all our men without delay."

At six o'clock that evening the Declaration of Independence was read to Washington's soldiers. When the reading was finished the men cheered wildly. They clapped each other on the back. They threw their caps into the air.

"Freedom!" one of them shouted. "Independence! That's worth fighting for, ain't it?"

"We'll take no more orders from old King George!" another one cried.

"Look at that statue of him over there in the park," yelled a third man. "Sitting on his horse and looking like he owned the world!"

"Let's tear him down!"

"Let's chop off his head!"

Yelling and shouting excitedly, the soldiers pulled over the heavy statue and knocked off its head. News of what they had done quickly reached George Washington.

That evening when everyone else in Washington's headquarters was in bed, the Commander in Chief sat down to write to his wife.

First he told her how much he missed her, and how he longed to be at home. Then he wrote about the Declaration of Independence.

[*149*]

And about what had happened to the statue of King George.

"I suppose I shall have to reprove the men for such conduct," he wrote. "But I shan't be severe. That statue, dear Martha, was made of lead! It will be melted down to make thousands of bullets."

He knew that his men would soon need all the bullets they could get!

[*150*]

## CHAPTER SEVENTEEN

## *The Old Fox Plays Hide and Seek!*

---

IT WAS Christmas morning. A bitter wind
swept over the floating ice which filled the
Delaware River. The tent was very cold.

Washington shivered and crawled out of his
camp bed. As he put on his clothes he thought
of Mount Vernon.

Servants would be lighting bright fires
there. Martha would be getting ready to help
Jack and his wife celebrate Christmas with
their children. For a moment he wished he
were with them. Then his mind turned to
other things.

Sitting down on the edge of the bed, he
pulled on his boots. They were worn and
shabby. But many of his soldiers did not even

have shoes. They had no warm clothing, and few blankets.

Again and again Washington had written to Congress asking for money to buy these things. He had even asked citizens to gather up old clothes for his ragged soldiers. But his men were still in a pitiful state.

Most of the men were discouraged. Some had already left the Army. Others were planning to leave when their time of enlistment was up. Soon he would have only a few troops left to carry on the war against the English Army.

And what an army that was! The angry English king had sent thousands of his finest soldiers across the ocean to teach the unruly Americans a lesson. He had also hired soldiers from a place called Hesse, in Germany, to help his redcoats.

Washington's little army was no match for King George's big one. And he knew it. But he smiled proudly when he remembered how bravely most of his men had fought to keep the redcoats from taking New York.

Yet the American soldiers had been badly defeated and driven from the city. Only Washington's quick thinking had saved them all from being captured. Since that time his army had been retreating across New Jersey, with the enemy following close behind.

Now Washington's men were camping in Pennsylvania near the Delaware River. Seven miles down the river, on the New Jersey side, Hessian soldiers were camped in a little village called Trenton.

"But they'll not be there long," Washington thought as he finished dressing. "Not if my plan for tonight succeeds."

*They climbed into boats and began their trip across
the ice-filled water*

He had already talked over this plan with his officers.

"We're not strong enough yet to stand and meet the enemy," he had told them. "But perhaps, if we use our wits, we can trick them.

"On Christmas night we'll march on Trenton. The Hessian soldiers will not expect an attack on a holiday. They'll drink extra rum to celebrate. And they'll probably sleep heavily. We should be able to take Trenton from them, if we can get there without alarming their sentries."

The plan had been well laid. And all that Christmas day Washington's men waited eagerly until dark, when they could begin to carry it out.

Dusk came at last. More than two thousand ragged American soldiers marched quietly to the bank of the Delaware River. Working in the dark, they loaded their cannon and horses on barges. Then they climbed into boats and began their trip across the black, ice-filled water.

Washington crouched in one of the crowded

[155]

boats. His nose was red with cold. His feet were almost freezing. He was worried about the attack, and uneasy about his men. Would they all cross the river safely?

They did! On the other side they fell into line.

"Up with firelocks!" Washington commanded. "Press on, boys. Press on!"

Up went their muskets against their shoulders. Tramp! Tramp! Off they marched toward Trenton.

Sleet and snow beat against their faces. Icy wind tore at their thin jackets and ragged cloaks. But they pushed steadily ahead. At dawn they reached the village of Trenton.

Suddenly a Hessian guard spied them advancing. "The enemy!" he shouted loudly. "Turn out! The enemy! Turn out!"

But his warning came too late.

Into the village rushed the Americans. And out of their tents stumbled the sleepy Hessians. The fight was a short one. When it ended the Americans had taken Trenton. They had captured more than eight hundred sturdy Hessians. And they hadn't lost one single man!

Washington was as joyful as his soldiers. He rode down the street on a big brown horse, looking over the town he had taken.

"A victory at last!" he exclaimed to one of his officers, who rode beside him. "It will give new hope to the Army and to the country. It's a glorious day, Major! A glorious day!"

But it wasn't a glorious day for the English. Eight hundred of their soldiers had been shipped across the Delaware as prisoners. In Princeton, ten miles away, an English general named Cornwallis was getting ready to punish the daring Americans.

Several days later he started off for Trenton with nearly six thousand redcoats. By nightfall English soldiers were camped on three sides of the town. The Delaware River ran swiftly on the fourth side. Washington and his men were trapped!

General Cornwallis chuckled to himself as he looked across the fields at the fires in the American camp that night.

"Now I have that rebel, Washington, where

I want him," he boasted to one of his officers. "I'll bag that old fox tomorrow."

Then he went into his tent and quickly fell asleep.

Meanwhile Washington and his officers were having a hurried meeting in the candle-lit kitchen of a farmhouse near by. Hastily the "old fox" was making plans to get out of his trap.

Late that night shadowy figures crept quietly among the men in Washington's camp. Sleeping soldiers were prodded awake and told not to make a sound. Their officers gave them whispered orders.

"We're leaving at once. No noise, now. Wrap all the rags you can find around the wagon wheels. They mustn't crunch in the snow.

"Watch the horses. Keep them quiet. Pile wood on your campfires. Leave them blazing to fool the English sentinels. Don't talk while you're marching. Not a sound! We're going to sneak away while the redcoats are sleeping."

Silently the men made ready. Silently the

American Army moved through the dark, around the sleeping enemy. Cornwallis and his soldiers did not know until morning that Washington and all his men had escaped.

In time of trouble good news travels quickly. Soon people all through the country were laughing over the story of how Washington had surprised the Hessians and fooled Cornwallis. Now they were prouder of him than ever before.

Even in foreign lands men who knew all about warfare were nodding their heads and saying, "There's a clever man. And a great leader."

Yet there were dangerous and difficult days ahead for Washington. Fighting did not begin again until late the next summer. But then the English marched toward Philadelphia. And, after several battles with the Americans, they captured it.

Philadelphia was a pleasant city. And the English settled down there to spend a comfortable winter.

Washington and his ragged, defeated troops marched slowly over icy roads to a tiny village twenty miles away. It was called Valley Forge.

*Alphabet & Dictionary.*

| Alphabet | a | b | c | d | e | f | g | h | i | j | k | l | m | n | o | p | q | r | s | t | u | v | w | x | y | z |
|---|---|---|---|---|---|---|---|---|---|---|---|---|---|---|---|---|---|---|---|---|---|---|---|---|---|---|
| Dictionary | z | y | x | w | v | u | t | s | r | q | p | o | n | m | l | k | j | i | h | g | f | e | d | c | b | a |

*Keep this alphabet and Dictionary always by you*
*Pvvh grrh Zohszyvg zmw Wrxgrlmzib zodzbh yb blf*

One of Washington's Private Cipher Codes

# CHAPTER EIGHTEEN

## *Cornwallis Meets His Match*

WASHINGTON picked up an apple which lay on his desk in his headquarters at Valley Forge. It was wizened and there was a large wormhole in it. But he bit into it hungrily. A moment later he turned to the young blue-eyed Frenchman who sat near him.

"I tell you, Marquis," he said, "if my men can live through this winter they can live through anything. They're freezing and starving and sick. Some of them have already deserted. And I often wonder why more don't try it."

The Marquis de Lafayette looked very sober. "It is because they have you for their general, sir," he said. "And because they have something to fight for."

Washington smiled. But before he could speak, the young Frenchman exclaimed eagerly, "The moment I heard of America, sir, I loved her! The moment I knew she was fighting for freedom I wanted to fight with her."

"And you've fought bravely!" Washington declared.

Already he loved this young Frenchman who had come from his own country to help America fight for liberty. He wished there were more men like him. For he needed all the help he could get.

Congress had been quick to blame him when Philadelphia had been captured by the redcoats. But slow to send him money for the food and clothing and weapons he needed desperately for his men.

Although he would not let his soldiers know it, he was weary and discouraged and homesick! He longed to see his wife and family. He had asked Martha to come to Valley Forge to spend the rest of the winter with him. Now he was waiting hopefully for her arrival.

It was a cold day in February when he saw

the big coach from Mount Vernon stop before his door. Then his plump little wife stepped out.

How glad he was to see her! He could hardly hide his joy from the eyes of the sentries who were standing guard. The moment he and his wife were alone together he caught her in his arms. When he let her go, she looked up at him anxiously. His eyes looked tired. And his hair was turning gray. She nodded her head wisely.

"It's just as I thought, my dear," she said, reaching up to touch his cheek. "You've been taking care of everyone but yourself. It's time now that someone took care of *you*."

Washington laughed and hugged her again. "Just seeing you makes me feel better!" he exclaimed. Then he began to ask questions about Mount Vernon. And about Jack and Jack's wife and children.

Soon Martha Washington was bustling busily about the camp. She visited sick soldiers in their tiny log huts. She knit dozens of stockings to cover their feet, which often left bloody tracks in the snow. She mended their old clothes. She made new ones. And she even had a little party now and then to cheer her husband and his officers.

Spring came late that year. But it came at last! The sun shone warmly. The Schuylkill River, near the camp, was filled with fish. Other food was now easier to get. Sick soldiers grew stronger. And everyone in Valley Forge began to feel better.

Then, one fine day in May, a messenger galloped into the camp with glorious news. Wonderful news from France.

For many months Benjamin Franklin had been trying to get France to send help to the thirteen United States. At last he had succeeded.

Money, ships, and soldiers, bound for America, were now on their way across the ocean!

Washington's eyes sparkled when he heard this news. In no time the camp was in a turmoil of rejoicing. Young Lafayette rushed up to General Washington, almost too happy to speak.

"Oh, my general!" he cried, grasping Washington by the arms. "We—we—my country and yours—we fight for the same thing!" And he kissed Washington quickly on each cheek.

There was a gay celebration in Valley Forge the next day, with marching and shouting. And three cheers for the King of France! And three cheers for the United States of America!

But the fighting was not over. Not nearly over. Even with all the help France sent, it dragged on for three long, dreadful years. There were hard-fought battles in the North and in the South. At last, during October, 1781, the French and the Americans together trapped Cornwallis and his army at Yorktown, in Virginia.

Cannon roared for ten days as the French and Americans bombarded the enemy's fortification. Then the English sent out a man with a white flag of truce. Cornwallis and his great army had surrendered!

Messengers galloped from Yorktown to spread the joyful news through all the country.

"Victory!" they shouted. "Cornwallis is beaten! The English have surrendered! Our country's free! We've won! We've won!"

But in Yorktown, General Washington shook his head. The war was not over yet. It would not be over until all the English soldiers had left the country. He still had work to do.

*Cornwallis and his great army had surrendered!*

There was no more fighting after the battle of Yorktown. But two years passed before the treaty of peace was signed.

Then the last English soldiers sailed home. The American Army was disbanded. At a big dinner in New York, General Washington took leave of the officers who had fought with him so bravely. And he started out on his journey home to Mount Vernon.

Cheering crowds met him all along the way. People pressed forward eagerly to get a glimpse of the man who had led his country through dark days to freedom.

"He's the greatest man in this land," they said to one another. "The greatest man in all the land."

# CHAPTER NINETEEN

## B-l-e-w Spells Blue

LITTLE NELLY CUSTIS didn't want to
have her hair combed. She wriggled and
squirmed and danced up and down. At last
her nurse gave her a gentle shake.

"If you don't stand still, I ain't never going
to get the snarls out of your curls," she declared. "And then what will your grandpappy
say?"

"He won't scold," Nelly replied. For almost a second she tried to stand still. Then
suddenly she jerked away from her nurse.

"Grandpapa!" she cried joyfully. Darting
across the room, she threw herself on the tall
man who had just appeared in the doorway.

George Washington swung her high in the

[*169*]

air and set her down again. With a puzzled frown she stepped back and looked him over from head to foot. She didn't like the plain blue coat and black knee breeches he was wearing.

"You're all different!" she exclaimed. "Where are your pretty soldier clothes?"

Washington laughed. "They're put away, Nelly, and I never want to see them again," he said.

He held out his big hand to a small boy who was playing on the floor.

"Come on, George Washington Custis, let's go downstairs," he coaxed. "I've a fine new whirligig for you to play with before supper. And there's a little book for Nelly to look at when she's had her hair combed."

With his small grandson holding tightly to his finger, he started down the stairs.

Nelly and little George were the children of Jack Custis. But Jack had died soon after the battle of Yorktown. And Washington had adopted both children.

He loved them as dearly as he had loved

their father. But he had not yet been able to spend much time with them. For his house had been full of company ever since he had reached home several weeks earlier.

Even now, as he walked downstairs with George, he could hear Martha talking to guests in the parlor. And a servant passed through the hall with a tray full of teacups.

Picking little George up quickly, Washington hurried to his library and shut the door. He was tired of visitors.

But he felt that he could not turn people away. And month after month they flocked to

[*171*]

Mount Vernon to pay their respects to the greatest man in the country.

All kinds of presents were sent to him, too. They came from different parts of the United States and even from abroad.

There were trees and plants for his gardens. Chinese ducks and pigs for his farms. Deer for a deer park. A pack of hunting dogs from his good friend Lafayette, who had returned to France. A long-eared jackass from the King of Spain. And countless other things.

Washington had to spend long hours with his secretary, writing letters of thanks for these gifts. He also wrote many other letters. Some of his letters were filled with worried remarks about his country.

Things were not going well at all in the thirteen States. The States had not yet learned to work together. They were not really united. Thoughtful men in each state were sorely troubled about this. At last, in the spring of 1787, they decided to meet in Philadelphia to discuss it.

[ *172* ]

So, one fine May morning, Washington said good-by to his family. And off he started for Philadelphia in his big cream-colored coach with its six beautiful horses. He did not return until September. Then he reached home one evening just as supper was ready.

Nelly and George came running down the steps to meet him. Martha Washington sent a servant to set another place at the table. And soon they were all in the dining room, with Nelly sitting on one side of her grandfather and George on the other.

"What did you do all the time you were away, Grandfather?" Nelly asked. "You were gone so long that George and I thought you'd never come back."

Washington laughed. "It seemed a long time to me, too," he said, unfolding his napkin. "But we did some good work in Philadelphia. We drew up a Constitution for the States."

"A Constitution!" George exclaimed, looking puzzled. "What's that?"

[*173*]

"It's a set of rules," Washington explained, helping himself to a hot biscuit. "When the States have agreed to obey those rules they will elect a President to govern the country. Then we'll really begin to grow into a strong nation."

Nelly looked admiringly at her grandfather. "I hope they'll make you President," she said.

Washington smiled and shook his head. "I hope they won't," he said quickly. "I'm a soldier, Nelly. And a farmer. I don't know how to govern a nation."

But the American people thought differently.

"We love Washington, and we trust him," they said to one another. "He never lost courage once, during the hard days of our war for freedom. He's the finest leader in the country. We want him for our President."

And so they elected him the first President of the United States.

On a beautiful day in April, George Washington made ready to set out for New York. For that was the capital of the country. Every-

[*174*]

one at Mount Vernon gathered near the steps to watch him leave.

At the door he turned to his wife and bent to kiss her good-by. "Come to New York as soon as you can," he said. "I'll be counting the days until I see you and the children again."

"We'll be there next month without fail," Mrs. Washington replied, brushing away some tears. "And don't worry, my dear. You'll be a splendid President. I know you will."

"I hope so," George Washington replied gravely. "The task is a tremendous one."

He kissed Nelly and held out his hand to George. "Good-by, lad," he said. "Take care of Nelly and your grandmother for me."

Turning quickly, he went down the steps and climbed into his coach. Then, waving again and again to his family and friends, he rode away.

It took him many days to reach New York. For, all along the way, people had prepared celebrations and parades in his honor. And when he reached the capital he was greeted by the most wonderful celebration of them all.

Every boat in the Hudson River was decked with flags. Houses were gaily trimmed with flowers and bunting. Guns boomed a welcome. Bands played loudly. Thousands of people, dressed in their best clothes, crowded the streets, cheering and shouting his name.

Three days later the celebration was still going on. And a huge crowd gathered in front of Federal Hall to hear Washington take the oath which would make him their first President.

Just after twelve o'clock that day, Washington stepped out on the balcony and laid his hand on a big Bible.

"I do solemnly swear," he said in a clear, strong voice, "that I will faithfully execute the office of President of the United States and will to the best of my ability, preserve, protect, and defend the Constitution of the United States."

The oath was finished. "Washington!" the people shouted, joyfully waving their handkerchiefs and their hats. "Long live our Presi-

*"Washington!" the people shouted joyfully. "Long live our President!"*

dent! Washington! Washington! Washington!"

The President looked at the people and smiled. He was glad that they loved and trusted him so. But he was afraid—terribly afraid that he would not make a good President.

"I'll just have to do the best I can," he thought. "The very best I can."

And that's what he did. For four years he governed the people so wisely and so well that they elected him for a second term. But when they asked him to be their President for a third term he shook his head.

"A man who is President for too long might some day want to be a king," he said. "And we're through with kings in this country forever."

Since Washington would not change his mind, the people elected John Adams to take his place. Sorrowfully they said good-by to George Washington.

Crowds lined the streets of Philadelphia, which had become the capital, to watch him leave the city. And, on the long drive home, people ran to see him pass. They cheered and shouted the name of the man who had been the first President of the United States.

When Washington reached home he found a host of friends and relatives waiting to welcome him. Indeed, for many days the house was so filled with visitors that it was hard for him to catch a moment alone with his wife. But one lovely warm spring afternoon he found her sitting in the portico. And he sank into an empty chair beside her.

A number of guests were gathered on the rolling green lawn talking and laughing together. George Custis and some friends were playing a game of rounders at the side of the house.

From the music room came the tinkling notes of Nelly's harpsichord. In the trees near the river, birds were singing sweetly. And beyond the trees, the deep blue water of the broad Potomac sparkled in the afternoon sun.

With a sigh of pleasure, George Washington looked around. For a long moment he stared at the river. Suddenly he chuckled. Mrs. Washington laid down her knitting.

"What are you laughing at?" she asked.

"Oh," said Washington with a smile, "I was just remembering a little boy on Ferry Farm who couldn't spell 'blue.'"

## "Names That Made History"

ENID LAMONTE MEADOWCROFT, *Supervising Editor*

THE STORY OF LOUISA MAY ALCOTT
By Joan Howard.           *Illustrated by Flora Smith*

THE STORY OF JOHN J. AUDUBON
By Joan Howard.           *Illustrated by Federico Castellon*

THE STORY OF CLARA BARTON
By Olive Price.           *Illustrated by Ruth Ives*

THE STORY OF GOOD QUEEN BESS
By Alida Sims Malkus.           *Illustrated by Douglas Gorsline*

THE STORY OF BUFFALO BILL
By Edmund Collier.           *Illustrated by Nicholas Eggenhofer*

THE STORY OF DANIEL BOONE
By William O. Steele.           *Illustrated by Warren Baumgartner*

THE STORY OF KIT CARSON
By Edmund Collier.           *Illustrated by Nicholas Eggenhofer*

THE STORY OF GEORGE WASHINGTON CARVER
By Arna Bontemps.           *Illustrated by Harper Johnson*

THE STORY OF CHRISTOPHER COLUMBUS
By Nina Brown Baker.           *Illustrated by David Hendrickson*

THE STORY OF CRAZY HORSE
By Enid LaMonte Meadowcroft.           *Illustrated by William Reusswig*

THE STORY OF DAVY CROCKETT
By Enid LaMonte Meadowcroft.           *Illustrated by C. B. Falls*

THE STORY OF GENERAL CUSTER
By Margaret Leighton.           *Illustrated by Nicholas Eggenhofer*

THE STORY OF STEPHEN DECATUR
By Iris Vinton.           *Illustrated by Graham Kaye*

THE STORY OF AMELIA EARHART
By Adele de Leeuw.           *Illustrated by Harry Beckhoff*

THE STORY OF THOMAS ALVA EDISON
By Enid LaMonte Meadowcroft.           *Illustrated by Harve Stein*

THE STORY OF LEIF ERICSON
By William O. Steele.           *Illustrated by Pranas Lapé*

THE STORY OF STEPHEN FOSTER
By Esther M. Douty.           *Illustrated by Jo Polseno*

THE STORY OF BENJAMIN FRANKLIN
By Enid LaMonte Meadowcroft.           *Illustrated by Edward A. Wilson*

THE STORY OF ULYSSES S. GRANT
By Jeannette Covert Nolan.                    *Illustrated by Lynd Ward*

THE STORY OF ANDREW JACKSON
By Enid LaMonte Meadowcroft.        *Illustrated by David Hendrickson*

THE STORY OF THOMAS JEFFERSON
By Earl Schenck Miers.                  *Illustrated by Reynold C. Pollak*

THE STORY OF JOAN OF ARC
By Jeannette Covert Nolan.                   *Illustrated by Pranas Lapé*

THE STORY OF JOHN PAUL JONES
By Iris Vinton.                         *Illustrated by Edward A. Wilson*

THE STORY OF LAFAYETTE
By Hazel Wilson.                          *Illustrated by Edy Legrand*

THE STORY OF ROBERT E. LEE
By Iris Vinton.                      *Illustrated by John Alan Maxwell*

THE STORY OF ABRAHAM LINCOLN
By Nina Brown Baker.               *Illustrated by Warren Baumgartner*

THE STORY OF MOZART
By Helen L. Kaufmann.                   *Illustrated by Eric M. Simon*

THE STORY OF FLORENCE NIGHTINGALE
By Margaret Leighton.                *Illustrated by Corinne B. Dillon*

THE STORY OF ANNIE OAKLEY
By Edmund Collier.                       *Illustrated by Leon Gregori*

THE STORY OF LOUIS PASTEUR
By Alida Sims Malkus.                        *Illustrated by Jo Spier*

THE STORY OF POCAHONTAS
By Shirley Graham.                       *Illustrated by Mario Cooper*

THE STORY OF MARCO POLO
By Olive Price.                    *Illustrated by Federico Castellon*

THE STORY OF THEODORE ROOSEVELT
By Winthrop Neilson.                 *Illustrated by Edward A. Wilson*

THE STORY OF MARK TWAIN
By Joan Howard.                        *Illustrated by Donald McKay*

THE STORY OF GEORGE WASHINGTON
By Enid LaMonte Meadowcroft.        *Illustrated by Edward A. Wilson*

THE STORY OF MARTHA WASHINGTON
By Jeannette Covert Nolan.           *Illustrated by Corinne B. Dillon*

THE STORY OF MAD ANTHONY WAYNE
By Hazel Wilson.                  *Illustrated by Lawrence Beall Smith*

1 Born February 22, 1732

2 Goes West as a Surveyor, 174[8]

3 Becomes master
of Mount Vernon, 1752

4 Serves under
General Braddock, 1755

10 Dies at
Mount Vernon,
December 14, 1799

9 Inaugurated first President
of the United States, 1789

8 Surrender of Cornw[allis]
Yorktown, 1781